Sir Alan Herbert was born in 1890 and
and Oxford. Having achieved a first in
joined the Royal Navy and served both at Gallipoli and in
France during the First World War. He was called to the Bar in
1918, and went on to become a Member of Parliament for
Oxford University from 1935 to 1950.

Throughout his life A P Herbert was a prolific writer,
delighting his many readers with his witty observations and
social satires in the columns of *Punch*. He was the creator of a
host of colourful characters – notably Topsy, Albert Haddock
and Mr Honeybubble – and wrote novels, poems, musicals,
essays, sketches and articles. He was also a tireless campaigner
for reform, a denouncer of injustice and a dedicated conserver
of the Thames.

By the time of his death in 1971, he had gained a
considerable following and was highly regarded in literary
circles. J M Barrie, Hilaire Belloc, Rudyard Kipling and John
Galsworthy all delighted in his work, and H G Wells applauded
him saying, 'You are the greatest of great men. You can raise
delightful laughter and that is the only sort of writing that has
real power over people like me.'

Topsy Turvy

A P HERBERT

HOUSE OF
STRATUS

This edition published in 2001 by House of Stratus, an imprint of Stratus Holdings plc, 24c Old Burlington Street, London, W1X 1RL, UK.

www.houseofstratus.com

Typeset, printed and bound by House of Stratus.

A catalogue record for this book is available from the British Library.

ISBN 1-84232-620-1

To
JACK AND JILL

CONTENTS

CONTENTS

LETTER I

PEACE!

October 10, 1945.

Trix, my restored exile, do you see a *ray* of hope, I mean all this *cosmic* acidity and gloom, it's *too* fraying, however *one* gleam is that you're back from Medicine Hat at *last*, or was it *Moose Jaw*, I forget, and I *do* grovel about my *utter* reticence while you were distant, only I merely could *not* write letters to the *remotest* places like Canada, I mean across *oceans*, and of course everything went round by *Cape* Horn or *Lapland* and took a *century*, so one thought Well, if *ever* this does touch Medicine Hat the chances are that *all* one's windows will have been detonated *again*, and the little old ashes may be at Golder's Green, *too* misleading, so it seemed the kindly thing not to utter at all, if you see what I mean, *not* to mention that *when* I imagined you and your *over-rated* young at work upon a *peach-fed* ham while *poor* Haddock and me were *prowling* hungrily from dust-bin to dust-bin, the little stomach missed *five* beats and the pen fell from the malnutritioned fingers, *besides* darling, you *must* comprend, life in the big city during the late conflict was a *shade* distractious and unadapted to *protracted* correspondence, my dear you *can't* imagine what the *doodle-bugs* were like, *quite* the most *unfriendly* gesture of the whole series, my dear Haddock and me were mere *magnets* for the pests, it seems they had a *wireless* attachment and simply

1

hounded some people about, the ones on the Black List I mean, which Haddock was it seems, and of course the instant one sat down to write you the *longest* letter those *emetical* sirens performed and one had to keep away from the *glass*, when we had any, and lie *flat* on the floor, but of course not *too* flat because of the blast effect on the old abdomen, the *most* complicated drill, darling, with the little rump *uplifted*, well if you scorned the action it was *too* likely you found yourself standing in the street with *utterly* no clothes on, my dear I've been prostrate in *all* the *wettest* gutters from the Savoy to *West London*, *rather* a strain on the wardrobe because of course *no* coupons allowed for gutter-work, but my dear Hermione Tarver, you remember her *surely*, she must be eighty now, was *too* meticulous about her *one* frock and was blasted *quite* naked in Church Street Kensington, *too* embarrassing, so it only shows, then of course we had *four* incendiaries on the roof, a *normal* bomb at the bottom of the garden, and the *most* malignant *rocket* three hundred yards away, however belay there, as Haddock says, I must desist and withdraw, because my dear, Haddock's already started this *morbid* anniversary habit, my dear the last fine Sunday we had which was *months* ago he came down to breakfast and said *Five* years ago I tied my ship up to a buoy marking a *mine*, to which of course the *one* response was How careless darling, which didn't ring any bells, and the next Sunday it was the *entire* Surrey Docks in flames, or the House of Commons *eliminated* or something, and my dear what with the anniversaries of the *last* war and the war before that, there's practically *no* day now which doesn't begin with some *gruesome* reminiscence, but my dear does he *ever* remember the twins' *birthday* not to mention his countless god-children's, not *ever*, not *utterly* ever, however *all* I was trying to say was, *Don't* be *too* wounded about my war-reticence, you do understand *don't* you poppet, then of course there was *security*, but I won't go into that now, only there *was literally nothing* you could say which mightn't give *nearly everything away*, even the *weather* was a septic theme, *except* in the Straits of Dover, and that I expect you saw in the papers.

It was *too* galling not to see you as you *flashed* through the city, but of course *if* it means you took *one* look at London and said to Henry, Gosh, no, *remove* me rapidly, I couldn't abuse you less, my dear isn't it the *zenith* of agony, or do I mean the *nadir*, anyhow I don't suppose for a moment you could have secured a *couch* anywhere, you have to give *years* of notice and then it's a guinea a minute, with 10 per cent for service and *no* service, and my dear of course *we're* utterly couchless because the *builders* are in, my dear they've *just* got round to the last bomb but one, not counting that *unethical* rocket which I must say they did *alacritously*, or some of it, but of course now I've painted the two top rooms for the twins they're *opening up* the roof and the *entire* sky will enter from now till Yule-time, *what* a life and it's the *most* seductive *cerulean* blue with *indications* of toe-nail pink, and then of course the *food*, my dear, I can't recall when I ate *last*, I mean *ate*, though of course doing *all* the cooking I never *want* to eat extensively, unless it's a *boiled* egg and we get them once a month *some* months, my dear *do* you remember the days when one tried to get the evening meal *too* late at some *insanitary* little hotel in a *cathedral* town and they said Sorry we've *only* got *breakfast dishes* and one turned up the little old nose at them, Gosh *only* breakfast dishes! *only* bacon and eggs and *kidneys*, and *do* you remember the County breakfasts when one *stalked* up and down the sideboard, *peering* haughtily at dish by dish, *spurning* kidneys on toast, *shuddering* away from *fried fish* and utterly *debating* whether one would *stoop* to a little sausage and bacon or stave off famine with *buttered* eggs and *mushrooms*, Oh dear of course Haddock says be doesn't think we shall *quite* ever see civilization again, well, not in *our* time, and by civilization Haddock means *hams*, I think he's *so* right for once, I mean a real *total* ham on the sideboard *always*, so that *whenever* the pangs of famine occurred one could *mutilate* the ham a piece and win through till the next meal, which *reminds* me darling of Haddock's *pet* song, I Do Like a Nibble in the Night, do you know it, because in the old days when he was *too* inspired he used to write novels and things *all night*, only when the *afflatus* failed there was always the *hugest* ham in the larder or at least a cold but enchanting leg of bird, and after a nibble and a noggin or two he'd perpetrate *four more chapters*, as it is the poor dear slinks muttering to bed and writes *practically nothing*, so perhaps there *is* something to be said for having *special* rations for *literary* households, however of course one can always *crawl* out to a restaurant, *if* you can get sitting-space, I don't say *food*, because my dear the *most* imperceptible gin costs half- or *three-quarters*-a-crown, and *if* they add the tiniest adjunct in the shape of flavouring, my dear the mere *dregs* of the grape-yard after the Wop-women have stamped out everything else with their *contagious* feet, well that sinks *four* shillings for a single sniff, and as for eatery one consumes *practically* nothing but *cats* and *dogs*, my dear *fried kitten* is *too* succulent *actually*, but one has one's *principles* well mustn't one, darling, and then of course *no* help in the home, when I tell you that *since* Alamein I've had *one* daily for two precarious hours, no more, and now of course what with her *redundant* husbands and sons all *swarming* back from the wars my *angelic* Mrs Bee is *so* fussed with feeding the soldiery that she has less and less time for your pathetic T, who is a blue mass of *varicosity* from *excessive* standing at the shop or sink, as of course are *all* the nation's matrons, but darling *don't* think for a *moment* that I'm *wilting* about having you, because *do* come *whenever* you like, of course it *won't* be the same as Medicine *Hat*, or was it Moose Jaw, but we'll manage somehow, and we *must* have the cosiest chat, O Gosh I've not told you a *thing* about the *twins* yet, and if one *can't* get a table anywhere one can nearly always find a *free* seat on the *Victoria*

Embankment or Sloane Square Station, and Haddock says I *do* make the most *filling* sandwiches out of *completely* nothing, so do come soon darling, farewell for a fraction, your *devoted* TOPSY.

LETTER II

CONSOLATIONS

October 17, 1945.

Well Trix, my *top* female, I've *just* a moment while the vegetables are doing, *no* I haven't, there's that *magnetic* dustman with the whole sack of *manure* he promised me from that *prolific* municipal horse sorry.

Here we are again, well I think you're *so* wise not to *think* of coming to stay in London *too* soon, because honestly *some* days one does *not* detect a *single* ray of hope, and as a *matter* of fact there's *no* doubt that *nearly* everything is worse than it was in the *war*, though as Haddock said during the late conflict, and my dear he has a *foul* habit of being *too* right, he *never* expected it to be anything else, of course the *bottom* blunder was to liberate that *tiresome* Continent, my dear you know I never did exactly *dote* on the foreigner, except the French perhaps because of *omelettes*, but really the *way* they're *all* behaving, my dear those divine but *inflated* Russians, and to think that we've to feed and foster the *obscene* Germans, who as Haddock said are the *sole* architects of the cosmic mess, well when I tell you that I still can't plant a *single* cutting or extract a *weed* without *lacerating* the little fingers with *broken* glass, we've collected *tons* but sometimes I think it's taken *root* or something and *grows*, well you'll *begin* to comprend perhaps how an *emaciated* matron feels when she reads *group*-letters asking her to *petition*

6

the Gov. to *reduce* her *too* imperceptible ration and send more to that *unnecessary* Continent, my dear of course you know my motto, I *always* say that it *always* pays to *always* do the Christian thing, but when it comes to *fats*, my dear *did* you know that we're sending absolute *tons* of fats abroad, when my dear if you gave me the *most* authentic and virginal *Dover Sole* tomorrow I could no more fry it than I could split an electron, *utterly* fatless, but my dear *what* do the French do except *consign* it to the *Black* Market, which is the *sole* thing it seems that my *adored* French are capable of *united action* in, and as for the *fraternal* Russians they *merely* remove everything they can see *fraternally* to Russia, my dear Haddock says we're the *Suckers* of the *World*, and of course if our wide-hearted *Americans* are going to weary in well-giving, and *could* you blame them, my dear that far from unmagnetic Mrs May we met in Jamaica *centuries* ago has been sending us fortifying little parcels *throughout* the conflict, well but *if* they do I suppose we shall *all* crawl about queueing for sea-weed and *dandelions*, which they say my dear are quite *startlingly* nutritious and everything, only even then I expect we shall send *most* of our sea-weed crop to that fallacious Continent, by the way darling you *know* my principles about bird-murder and everything but I'm absolutely open-minded when the bird's in the *oven*, so one day if Henry comes tottering home with any *superfluous* feathered things from the moors or spinneys you *won't* forget the wolf at a certain door in West London, will you?

However darling *don't* think for a moment that I'm weakening, or anything, because there *are* one or two quite *positive* consolements, well, for one thing the twins are safe thanks be and blooming, and then nowadays one need *simply* never listen to the News *at all*, because you know for *certain* that there *can't* be any *good* news and the one wagerable thing *is* that you'll hear some lugubrious trumpet of the people miffling away about everything being *too* impossible and we must tighten the old belt *again*, well my dear if you could *see* the little belt it's *nothing* but holes and *nearly* goes *twice* round the midriff, my dear yesterday I *weighed* the meagre body on Haddock's *parcel*-scales and it seems I could be posted for *about* fourpence-halfpenny, besides if you *do* listen it's practically bound to be that dogmatic *announcerrr* who talks about Russ-i-a, puts four r's into *destroyerrrr*, and one into Malaya-r, only of course *when* in a hurry he *forgets* about his r's *like* you and me, which only shows how *fundamentally* bogus, however then I *must* say there *is* a *touch* of anodyne in going to bed *undressed*, *not* expecting to hear *rude* explosions or be blown into the *basement*, and *not* leaving the bath-water in the bath for *incendiaries* which looks *too* degrading and *insanitary* in the cold wet *dawn*, and of course *no* black-out which *is* my dear the absolute *ecliptic* of bliss, which perhaps will *show* you *how* low we've sunk in these *barbarous* years, because I mean *literally*, no Haddock says I mean *actually* if anything, I *never* look at a *lighted* window without a *positive* thrill, and my dear to this *day* if I come home latish and switch on the *smallest* light I still think O Gosh the *police* I *never* did the fatiguing *black-out*, and of course *not* having to creep about *stealing* electric torches, *colliding* with lamp-posts, falling over *sand-bags*, or butting into the bosoms of *revolting* strangers, my dear it's *Paradise*, the only bleak point in *this* Borough is that they've given us the *most* bilious *blue* street-lighting, which makes the *whole* population look like film-stars *made up*, my dear the lipstick goes *quite* black, *too* macaber, of course I dare say *all* this sounds *absolute* bats to you, because I suppose the black-out was comparatively *formal* in Medicine *Hat*, or *even* Moose Jaw, but *six* years darling do seem to go on for *quite* a time and *this* frail matron has *never* left the risky city, so you'll comprend perhaps our simple pleasures, personally of course I *sometimes* sigh for the bad old days, I mean the peak-weeks of the *doodlebugs* or the 1940 *winter*, when swarms of the citizens were rightly *too* elsewhere, one could *move* about the city and even from time to time secure a *meal*, my dear in the doodle-days I've seen the *Savoy*

Grill *half* empty at 1.30, and Haddock says *one* day he went into a club and they positively *thrust* fried sole and *salmon* at him, *now* of course the *entire* town is *one* mass of *redundant* personnel with *nothing* to do it seems but *swarm* about the pavements, *monopolize* the taxis, *congest* the Underground, and *minister* to the alimentary *canal*, my dear *where* they've all *emerged* from and *what* they're all *for* I definitely can *not* envisage, of course it's *too* futile to *think* of lunching much after 11.30 anywhere, and by that time the main dish is *generally* off, and as for *movement* well the *bizarre* thing is that the *more* Americans go away the *fewer* taxis and *one* theory is that they're taking them *home* with them, and *as* for the Underground they used to talk about the *Rush-hour* but which it is now it's *too* impossible to say, and my dear all the *largest* soldiers accoutred with *everything* poor pets, which reminds me darling when you *do* come up I can't *utterly* guarantee that you won't have a *rather* shattering *voyage*, because they say *some* of the trains are more like *Belsen* every day, my dear a man I know who stood to *Holyhead* in the corridor said he *knew* now, what the *Poles* had suffered, if I were you darling before you start I should *train* for the train, I mean *stand* for an hour or two in some small asphyxiating *cupboard* to get the corridor-technique and *fortify* the unaccustomed legs, and *don't* on *any* account let Henry take *Firsts* because *they're* all occupied by the *most* carbolic and unmelting types with Thirds, there'll only be *needless* antagonism, and Henry will have *frustration* as well as the cramp, *too* lowering.

However angel in *spite* of all the *turmoil* of Peace you'll find us *quite* bonhomous and even *jocular*, that's one thing, when you *know* you've *nothing* to look forward to it's so much less of a *worry* isn't it, I mean than when you're always *hoping* for the next thing like in the war, because now one sort of *trickles* about in a *genial* coma, *utterly* thankful for *small* things like *stewed* cat or switching on a light, and my dear I must say the people on the whole are *quite* wonder-worthy considering all things, *not* forgetting the *worn* legs and varicose veins, I mean *how* the bus-conductors stand it I *cannot* guess, and you can ask almost any one the way without getting a rude response, which is more than I can say about the General Election, I must tell you about *that* degrading episode, but no more now, because my *vegetables*, farewell, and come when you can, your suffering TOPSY.

LETTER III

THE SUFFRAGE EPISODE

October 24, 1945.

Trix, Hen of the North, *uncountable* thanks for the poor wee
feathered thing, which was *absolutely* eatable and cheered these
jaded *oesophaguses* noticeably, yes darling I *know* you sent a
brace, but only *one* got through a *little* mangled, however that's
a pretty high proportion for these days, *after* all it's *fifty* per cent
isn't it, and I found two moving little *shots* in my piece which
made me think of Henry *slinking* through the spinneys in that
filth of a coat, the bloodthirsty old bag, however top salutes to
both and Haddock says he's not against bird-murder *any* more.

But I promised to tell you about that *rancid* Election, my
dear you know I've seen a good deal of the suffrage-stuff in my
time, and of course one does *not* expect an Election to be as
boracic as a charity bazaar, but honestly *this* time the old
fatherland did touch bottoms for behaviour, I don't mean the
result, but my dear *one* minute the whole nation were beavering
away together, *quite* bosoms except for a few carps among the
politicos, and the next there was *mass*-rudery and vinegar
everywhere, my dear a *railway*-porter at Burbleton told Joyce
Pennant who's *half*-crippled she could *carry her own bag*, my
dear the *sweetest* porter with *velvet* manners as a rule and now
all smiles and service again, which thanks be goes for most of
the populace, but *for* a period it was *too* like *shaking* a bottle or

11

stirring up the mud-bed of Haddock's *newt-pond*, the *most* unexpected *smells emerged* from the mere *dregs* of the Island character, my dear the most *brutal* tale was about John Penny, *you* know the blind *Member*, well he was answering some imbecile questions quite bonhomously as he *always* is, my dear he *is* Galahad, and he said to one man I *think* I see what you mean, *whereupon* some young Briton at the back sings out, *You* can't see *anything* You're *blind*, my dear *can* you imagine such a mind, and of course as Haddock says if *that's* the fruits of seventy years of free State *education* it may well be that our *arrangements* need *drastic* attention, I mean, he says, look at *Newfoundland* where education is *too* far astern according to *us*, because it seems it's all run by the *Churches*, *three* in number, *not* counting the Salvation Army, so that the *minutest* village has three or four little schools with not enough teachers or money or *anything*, and it's all *too* overlapping and undeorientated and everything, on the *other* hand there are *no* policemen and *no* crime, there's *one* murder about every ten years and the *whole* population have manners like *Archangels* or spaniel puppies, so it *may* be the old State doesn't know *quite* all it thinks it does, do you see what I mean darling?

However where was I, well to go back to this *leprous* Election, well my dear as a *matter* of fact, I wasn't *fanatical* about Haddock standing *at all* this time, after all we've each had *five years* in that Place, and after all this war-nonsense it's *high* time he settled down and a wrote a trilogy or something if only to nourish the suffering *twins*, after all my dear I married a young *barrister*, but what happens he takes up this precarious *writing*, then without warning he became a *politico* the lowest form of vegetable life, *not* content he goes for a sailor again and spends the entire war doing semaphore and *logarithms*, and my dear what with getting his *latitude* and renaming the stars I *can't* envisage *why*, one *literally never* knows what new horror may not corrode the horizon *any* day, and *none* of them so far as I can see having the *feeblest* effect on the cosmos not to mention the little old *overdraft*, and Mr H himself I think was fairly unfanatical about it himself and sighed somewhat for the old life *mainly* based on the *Study* and the *Local*, however it seemed the done thing to do, to stand I mean, so there it was, well of course we had a *rationally* calm passage ourselves, apart from addressing *thirty* thousand *putrescent* envelopes *and* filling same with Haddock's *interminable* Address, my dear I know a man who's *still* reading it, in *bed*, *doggedly*, but after that well you can spurn the ancient Universities if you *like*, but they *do* have the *sole* civilized election habits, my dear there are *no* meetings, *no* speeches, no *posters*, *no* committee rooms, my dear Haddock hasn't even got a *Committee*, because he says *if* you have a *Committee* at *any* moment they may *mass* together and proclaim that they've lost *all* confidence in you, whereas not *one* person has *ever* expressed *any* confidence in Haddock, which I think is *so* right, so at least *nobody* can say he's lost it, and my dear *all* you do is to write down *everything* you think about everything and *weigh* it, yes I *mean* weigh it darling because it has to be under 2 ounces or $^1/_4$ oz. for the troops, and then if your opinions don't weigh *too* ponderously you merely discharge them into the Post Office and pray, and my dear *when* you think of the *squalor* and *torment* of the normal Election my dear *continual* mouth-work, I know people who made *seventy* speeches, and at the end they said they felt like *filthy* sponges, dank and degraded, well when Haddock had been safely delivered of his Address we *circled* about helping in six other places, well when I say *helped* at least *four* of the six were *outed* so who knows but my dear the *meetings*, either sleeping-parties or shouting-matches, and of course *all* the open-airs were arranged to take place on Saturday evening in the rain *too* close to the *largest* pub, and the un-Christian soldiery would cluster outside the pub with *copious* tankards, pay *no* attention to anything said and make the *most* irrelevant *long-range* interruptions, and of course *since* their vote if any was *miles* elsewhere they were *simply* sabotaging the truth from the local

votery, who my dear being *mere* civilry sat *mute* as mice, and of
course if *any* speaker so much as ventured to say to some *vocal*
warrior Sir *have* you a vote in this division, there was *complete*
uproar mutiny and *dis*affection, and honestly my dear *when* I
think *how* they behaved and *how* they treated that *sympathetic*
James Grigg who Haddock says was the best War Secretary the
old cow Britannia has had for *generations*, and the *first* one who
won a *real* battle for *several* wars, well honestly I could bear it
if some of them were *never* demobilized or anything ever, poor
pets, well then of course there was the *unique* Mr — at
Longbottom Nearly where George Pixton got in again in *spite*
my dear of Haddock making *six* speeches in aid of him, well this
Mr — said that he was for Churchill *too* but *independent*, well
quite all he did was to harry and molest poor *George*, my dear
he had a *hired* gang of soldiery who *hounded* George from
meeting to meeting, *asking* always the *same* synthetic questions
from *typewritten* slips, which of course is *so* spurious, and my
dear *all* the questions were about their *unimportant* stomachs, I
mean did *one* man ever yell *What* about the *Empire*, and *then*
my dear Mr — went *round* the town *daily* in a loud-speaker van
booming viperously GEORGE PIX-TON IS A LI-AR –
GEORGE PIX-TON et-cet-er-a, the evidence for which
assertion being *quite* fallacious and *non-existent*, because *I saw*
the *telegrams*, well poor George at last distributes a *writ*, or
whatever is the done thing to do with writs, but after the
Election he has to *withdraw* it, because it seems by the *infantile*
law of libel and so forth when it's a *spoken* slander you have to
prove *damage* which as George *won* he couldn't, and that will
show you what the *law* is, I mean when you can shout *carbolic*
insults through a *loud*-speaker for *days* on end *without* a come-
back, in the Courts I mean, because thanks be Mr — *did* lose his
festering deposit, well finally there was *Deathsend* where
Haddock spoke at the Eve of the Poll meeting in the *most*
scrofulous Market to two thousand citizens, some alien soldiery
and a *mercenary* gang of hoolies who *with* the soldiery *quite*

dominated the proceedings, well when I tell you that Haddock is one of Deathsend's *most* ancient allies, my dear he *opened* their obscene Municipal Baths *before* the war and *with* the Mayor threw a ceremonial blonde into the Bath, not to mention he was *always* disembarking at Deathsend during the late conflict, so he did think in *spite* of the form that possibly he *might* get as far as L and G it's good to be in *good* old Deathsend again, but my dear *far* from it, they *howled* miscellaneously for *five* minutes before he could *utter*, so at last, wearying slightly, he *yelled* into the microphone, *How* many of you have been *paid* for making this *criminal* din, hands up, well my dear *two* well-trained hirelings at *once* put their hands up, at which Haddock says he laughed so much he nearly *gravitated* off the platform, but then he shouted Jolly good show any advance on *two* and three more citizens put *their* hands up, which Haddock found *so* stimulating that *in* the end he shouted them *down* and said *much*, though I need *not* say that his Candidate was *quite* out, altogether perhaps you'll begin to sniff the general *aroma* of the suffrage episode, and *although* no doubt we've got the best Government *ever* one did *just* wonder sometimes if it wasn't a queer way to choose a *Parliament*, or even a dog, however, no complaints, I must say they're *all* welcome to their hot seats, *what* a job, farewell your unstateswomanlike TOPSY.

LETTER IV

THE MOON PARTY

November 1, 1945.

Trix, darling, I couldn't care *less* about the atomic bomb could *you*, I mean on *all* the evidence it's a *fairly* drastic and straightbackward proceeding, there are *no* queues for it, *no* coupons are required it seems, one will *not* spend the rest of one's life weeding *broken* glass from the flowerbed, there are *no* r's in it so one will *not* be rendered raving by my *favourrrrite* announcerrr's announcements about it, the desirability of the cosmos is *quite* dubious anyhow, and my dear as Harry said it was *too* laughable when the old atomic emerged how *all* the woolliest and wettest of the population at *once* vociferated Well *this* will clear the cosmic mind at last, and *then* my dear settled down to talk the *same* wool and wet as they had talked for *centuries*, well now for example they're *dismembering* the American Pres because he won't show the Secret to suffering *Russia*, and no wonder suffering Russia is suspicious and everything if *that's* how the brutal capitalists behave, etc., when my dear if there *is* one thing more patent than another it is that you *won't* get *many* kind words out of suffering Russia, *whatever* you do, well my dear *suppose* the Americans said OK we'll *share* the Secret with *simply* everyone, it's too easy to envisage how suffering Russia would respond *at* once, it would be *There* you go again, giving *all* my neighbours the know-how, so as to build

16

the *most* unmatey atomic wall *against* me, *personally* of course
I'd make it all *quite* public, if only because *if* one's going to be
obliterated there's something to be said for having it done
professionally and *well*, with *notice*, whereas my dear as long as
it's a naughty secret it's *too* likely you'll have old men fumbling
about in the mountains and deserts and blowing up the cosmos
messily without a word of warning, which *perhaps* was what
Einstein had in mind, my dear *did* you see, the old wizard said
it was *quite* erroneous that the atomic conflict would be the *end*
of civilization, because he said we should be *merely* terminated
about *two-thirds* and there'd be enough *books* surviving
probably for the residuary chaps to start *all over again*, which
you must agree darling is *about* the most *lowering* utterance of
the *whole* series, because my dear *can* you envisage your little
Topsy *waking* up *quite* naked in a dank jungle *miles* away and
starting again on the New York Evening Post and the Swiss
Family *Robinson*, no thanks *no*, by the way darling don't whisper
a *thing* because I gather it *is* pretty confidential still but it seems
there is a *definite* movement to evacuate *some* of the British to
another *planet*, or at least to start a pilot *colony*, I mean to found
a New World *literally*, I *won't* swear but I *think* it's the Moon,
which I believe is *too* feasible because *once* you've got the old
atomry in *full* action you can *fertilize* deserts and make *granite*
nutritious, then of course all these *fantastic* jet-machines, my
dear they'll be *so* fast it seems you'll be *in* the stratosphere the
day before you *start*, if you see what I mean, the *one* snag I
believe has been about reaching the Moon *too* fast because of
gravity or something, but now they've got round *that* even by
Radar, because my dear there's *utterly* nothing you *can't* do by
Radar, well it seems by Radar you set up a *resistance*-cushion in
the Moon on *which* my dear you come down *too* cosily like the
Black Duchess *planing* into a Charity bazaar, however darling
don't press me for *all* the details, the stark thing is that the *Plans*
are ready, but my dear *apart* from the Red Tape, which
Haddock says has been *without* precedent, the *usual*

stumbling-blocks at once obtrude, and *that* is *Shall* we tell the suffering *Russians*, because of course they'll be *too* suspicious and wounded about the enterprise, and for *all* we know they may have a *secret* eye on the Moon themselves, or some say *Mercury*, though of course we're *not* likely to hear *many* details in advance if they *have*, however it seems we'd be *most* amenable to unfold *all* if it will help to keep the cosmos sweet, but the drear thing is of course that *if* we tell the suffering Russians we shall have to tell the soft-eyed *Americans*, and then the Yanks will want *bases* all over the Moon, *not* to mention *platoons* of observers, there'll be all that *stupefying* dollar-nonsense again, my dear you *know* I'm not *congenitally* international but *why* we can't *all* use the *same* coins I definitely can *not* envisage, and then I suppose the first babies in the Moon will be *born* chewing, if *not* crooning, which much as I love them, my dear you *should* have seen Eisenhower and Mark Clark taking their degrees at Oxford, my dear what *pets*, what *natural* magnets, as I've told Haddock if either of them raised the *merest* finger I'd be an export *at* once, on the other hand I do think that the New World perhaps *should* start on the right foot, that is *rather* British and *no* chewing, because I do feel that a chewing child in a *New* World might spoil *half* one's pleasure, altogether it *does* look sometimes I gather as if this *utterly* idealistic plan might be merely *one* more nigger in the cosmic *woodpile* if it's *not* handled like one's monthly egg, that is pretty *maternally*, however we shall see, meanwhile Haddock and me are on the *Shadow* List for Founder Members and soon I suppose we shall have to *make* up the reluctant *mind*, what do you think darling shall we *go*, of course if it could be a real nest of *suitables* it might be *quite* Heaven getting *away* from everything, my dear these *builders*, I suppose you'd never *seduce* your Henry from his heaths and spinneys and I *can't* promise *much* about the *shooting* in the Moon, in fact Haddock's a *little* dubious about the *boating* because nobody *really* knows about the *canals*, or is that *Mars*, on the other hand it's *not* like

Australia one gathers where you have to *saw* your way into the Bush, or out of it, and of course with the *atom* in your hand you can *practically* have what *scenery* you *require*, I mean you make a *lake* here and a mountain *there* and grow what you *like* in them, so I don't suppose it would be *too* long before we fitted the male appendages with the customary pursuits and hobbies, but of course the *key*-thing is to have the *right* category *personnel*, and my dear *if* the New World is going to be *peopled* with Youth Movements, Government Departments, observing *Senators*, *chewing* children and jitterbugging *soldiery*, and of course *if* the *entire* place is to be run *half* like a Borstal and *half* like a quick-lunch canteen, which Haddock says *is* civilization today, then perhaps there is *something* to be said for clinging to the old familiar planet during its *few* penultimate *years*, and *by* the way there is *one* thing that *when* the Big Bang happens even the *Moon* may not be *too* salubrious because of proximity, however I do think that if one's going to be as *meticulous* as *all* that one would never get *anywhere*, well don't you agree.

So there it is, I must *desist* now darling because I'm dining with Haddock at the *House*, first time since the New Era and *quite* a thrill, that is if he gets a *table* which I believe is *generally* prohibitive, because my dear it seems the old place has become a popular *resort*, not only do all the new Members spend the *entire* day on the premises, *not* having a mass of clubs like the old school it seems, but *all* their constituents swarm upon them daily, *eager* for seats in the Gallery or beer, which Haddock says is *too* gratifying because for years he's been urging the populace to *take* an interest in the despised *talking*-shop, and now it seems they *do*, which of course is *one* valid result of that *fallacious* Election, however no more now darling, you might *sound* Henry about your coming on the *Moon*-party, don't tell him a word of *course*, only the general outline, as it were, farewell your faithful TOPSY.

LETTER V

FRUSTRATION

November 7, 1945.

Well Trix old evergreen we were *too* right about your *not* coming, because my dear these *builders*, I'm a mere *maze* of frustration and trouble, my dear I *sometimes* think I'm heading for the new *peace*-neurosis which is congesting *half* the nursing-homes, it's not *too* certain we shall get far with this epistle now, no there's another bell, oh what is it *now*.

That my dear was that *melting* man with the dog-like eyes from the Town Hall Mr Fisk, and it seems the plumber's mate has merely *declined* duty and gone to the dogs or pictures, my dear *what* a job Mr Fisk I mean, because he's the poor martyr in charge of *bomb*-repairs and my dear sooner than that I'd *volunteer* to sit in the House of Commons *all* day and listen to *all* the speeches, and *if* you recall how well-developed my powers of *speech-resistance* are that will show you perhaps, well I dare say all this will sound to you like the whistling of *bats* because of course you've no *conception* of peace-conditions up there in the pampered North, but the *basic* horror is that one's *own* builder is *too* illicit, I mean you remember my boracic Mr *Mason*, I'm sure you do because my dear the day you got locked in the lav he came and *redeployed* you, well for *centuries* when there's been the *least* home-trouble, my dear from porous walls to stubborn obstacles in the *sink*, one merely hoisted the Mason

20

signal and *there* he rapidly *was*, of course there'd be *estimates* and all that ritual, but things did utterly *happen*, my dear there is not *one* square centimetre of this humble ruin that Mr Mason has *not* patched up or painted or played with at one time or another, my dear it's like Stone*henge* to him, the merest *hint* of wet-rot keeps him *awake*, my dear he erected our sandbag-shelter in 1938 which by the way *collapsed* theatrically the very *day* the war took place in *1939*, however, sorry darling, another blistering *bell*.

That of course was the *piano-tuner* who my dear has an *enviable* genius for arriving *quite* unheralded on the *wrongest* day, my new still-life chrysanthemums group *majestically* arranged have to be *banished* from the instrument and *plasterers* in the room, however there's a *dim* hope he may drive the builders into a *frenzy* about which I should be *quite* neutral, because *as* I was telling you Mr *Mason's* men were *all* locals and *too* congenial, my dear they knew *all* the gossip on *all* the neighbours, they remembered the *twins* when they were *one* inch long, there was one *celestial* old carpenter who Haddock says would have done *just* as well as the Archbishop of Canterbury and *looked* it *better*, then of course Mr Mason himself was always BEE*ing* in and out to see that things were maturing, though *quite* needless because my dear the men *took an interest* and toiled like *yeomen*, one sustained them with beer and bonhomy and all proceeded fraternal and *effective*, however *now* my dear the picture is *too* otherwise because for *bomb*-repair Mr Mason is *quite* out-of-bounds, my dear I was *practically* arrested for ringing him the morning after our *rocket*, which *by* the way descended *punctually* in the *early* morning after our *wedlock* anniversary party, my dear Haddock lay in a *classic* stupor and simply *never* heard the thing *at all*, which *when* I tell you that it was the *loudest* missile *just* across the river not *three* hundred yards from the home was not perhaps a startlingly good *show* as from time to time he *half*-acknowledges, as for me I woke up to find the trembling frame *encrusted* in plaster from the ceiling and glass in *all* our quarters for the *fourth* time, well in the dank dawn we waded through glass to the long-talker and got the faithful Mr Mason round, well *he* got a *licence* or thought he did to stave off the elements with cardboard and such, my dear for *years* one lived in *electric* light and *looked* like one of those synthetic *mushrooms* in a cellar, and then of course they couldn't trace *who* had said Proceed, and for quite a time there was almost *national* unpleasantness because as I know now *painfully* the done thing is to wait till they send you someone from the *Pool*, and the Pool my dear at the *present* time seems to be a gang of *non*-local *non*-labourers, *mainly* imports from the *swamps* of Ireland, who my dear could *not* care less if this Borough had *never* existed and remained in ruins *now*, they're *too* uninterested in *us*, they're *not* paid by the builders, they're *not* his men, and think he's getting *rich* on them, because of cost plus or something, they merely *milk* and mock at the Council, and *we* don't pay anyone so can't utter a *word*, except of course to my *poor* Mr Fisk who is quite beside himself with care and thwartment, *beavering* wistfully to get all this *pond*-labour to *labour* from time to time, and of course as Haddock says as an advertisement of State what-is-it it is *not* spectacular, because my dear *when* you think that the *last* relevant missile descended more than *ten* months ago and the *roof's* still quite undone, not to mention a *precarious* chimney which is *too* likely to *dive* into the top bedroom if it blows *at all* Haddock says, of course I *know* they had to do the *top* things first and of course *labour* and *wood* and everything is *too* insufficient, *all* one wonders is that *anything* gets done under the *pond* system, well my dear for *twelve* days they've been at work on our *blasted* conservatory, well when I say *at work*, my dear at 8.30 two soporific Irish types arrive and have a *prolonged* smoke, at 9 or later two more come *sometimes* and *one* morning they all toiled *madly* till 11.30, at *which* point there was a *general* exodus, returning my dear at a quarter-to-two, two of them, so my dear you can see the Civil Service luncheon hour is spreading *vertically*, however *more* often what happens is that only *two* toilers appear at all the carpenter and the plumber's *mate*, or sometimes the plumber and the *carpenter's* mate, which my dear means *utter* inanition because it seems the carpenter can't *move* without his *mate* and the plumber's *mate* is *too* powerless without his *plumber*, the point about the *plumber* darling is that the *bathroom* waste *emerges* down a pipe on top of the conservatory *which* being now removed *no* bath is feasible without a *cascade* of soapy water into the *conservatory*, *too* alarming, well of course in the *normal* outfit the carpenter would merely *ring* Mr Mason and say Oy we're stagnant, but my dear in *these* proceedings far from it, they're *too* content to sit about the garden enjoying the view and smoking *endlessly*, my dear I can *not* guess *where* they obtain such *multitudinous* cigarettes, and the next day probably it's a *different* two but they're waiting for *material*, which for all we know may be *too* true, however from time to time if one ventures to take an interest, and Haddock says it's not *too* safe, one rings up the Town Hall and tells poor Mr Fisk one's got two *stagnant* toilers in the garden, but by *that* time of course they've quietly *vanished*, to the local one presumes, well in the afternoon perhaps a *foreman* visits the scene and then if any toiler has returned there's the *most* corrosive wrangle about their *rights* and everything, because it seems on this work they get only *union* rates while similar toilers are getting *bonuses*, which is rankling as one must admit, and by the end of that it's time to put the old tarpaulin over and *withdraw* exhausted, my dear this morning Saturday three toilers attended and sawed and hammered for *quite* half an hour, but my dear they've dispersed *already*, at 11 sharp *away* the toilers went not to return praises be, perhaps it was the piano-tuner, well *after* all this to the *lay* eye the conservatory looks *too* like what it looked like last *Monday*, after the first assault, the *one* difference is that the garden is a *sea* of *chips* and corrugated iron and one of the Irish citizens *inflamed* about his rights fell into Haddock's little pond *quite* wrecking the *last* water-lily of the season, *too* cruel, the *one* gleam is that when you get two *English* locals alone they seem to toil in the ancient fashion, my dear the *painters* are *utter* pets, so perhaps there is *one* ray of hope, and my dear I'm *not* suggesting that our landlord's conservatory is a *top* priority in the Reconstruction and the Worthier World, *all* I say is *if* it's to be done well *do* it because as Haddock says *if* this is a small categorical example it's *too* lowering to think of all the public money that must be ambling down the drain, not to mention the Irish, and *how* they hope to build a *single* house at this rate, and my dear when I think of all that *fallacious* drip about the *profit* motive and how the toiler toils with a *whistle* in his heart when he knows he's toiling for the *community* and not for a *shark-souled* employer like my beloved Mr Mason, well *then* my dear I feel sometimes like hiring one of those *odious* loud-speaker vans and going for a ride round London saying the *rudest* things, O dear, farewell your far from unfrustrated TOPSY.

LETTER VI

IODINE DALE

November 14, 1945.

Trix darling about the *Moon*-Party, you remember I said you
might *sound* your Henry a bit, about the *evacuation* I mean, well
I do *hope* you weren't *too* communicative because it's *quite* off
the *whole* thing, my dear *just* as I foretold *pure* international
jaundice prevailing *ubiquitously*, my dear the suffering Russians
wouldn't think of *anyone* proceeding to the Moon *at all*, the
Americans wanted *ten* Moon-bases, the Australians it seems had
never been consulted, the Canadians needed *all* the mining-
rights, the *entire* tribe of Smaller Nations *not* to mention the
whole of South America *insisted* on having a *Joint* Committee
not to mention *observers* and moon-dromes, so my dear by the
end of the Conference the *one* country with practically *no* claim
on the Moon was *poor* old Britain, who conceived the entire
thing, anyhow it's *quite* off now darling, and perhaps there *is*
something in Haddock's couplet If Drake had waited for
Whitehall He never would have sailed at all, *too* discouraging.

But I was going to tell you about my pathetic *Iodine*, you
remember her *don't* you, Iodine *Dale*, she captained *lacrosse* or
something at the old academy, well my dear *too* carelessly she
married a *most* dank and insanitary species, my dear I *can't* tell
you everything in a *letter*, but anyhow the total effect of the
union was *atomic*, *mere* disintegration and septic vapours,

25

however she's got her divorce poor dear or rather she *hasn't*, because of course *all* she's got is this childish decree *nisi*, and *nisi* little rustic I *must* inform you is a *Latin* word signifying *unless*, and when you think of the *thousands* that occur each year well *that* as Haddock says will show you how *dead* the Latin language is, well anyhow Iodine has got this decree of divorce *unless*, and my dear *if* you ask Haddock unless *what*, *all* he can say is *unless* the Judge changes his *mind*, and of course *put* like that it shows up doesn't it how *intensely* spurious, because at *once* you ask why *should* he change the little old mind, and then he says Oh well there might have been *collusion* or *connivance* or *condonation* or one of *those* things, well then I said but *why* didn't the Judge discover such banes and blemishes at the *trial*, so then Haddock said As a *matter* of fact you're *too* right, that's just what he's *supposed* to do, well my dear by *this* time the little head was circulating somewhat, so Haddock gave me the longest explanation which I'll *try* to repeat for you in rustic language, and my dear *don't* think that this is merely *lawyers'* fun because here under my *anaemic* wing *is* this distracted Iodine, half-*bats* with worry *although* the innocent party, policemen at the back door, and macaber figures *lurking* in the shadows, what's more you or yours may be in the same ditch any day *no* darling I withdraw of course your Henry could *never*, *half* a minute I *must* take a peep outside to see if that *man* is under the lamp-post again.

Yes there he is, *too* fraying, it's the cockeyed lamp the *rocket* blasted, and now I suppose it will *never* be mended, he *leans* against the lamp-post on the shadow side and you *just* can't see his *repulsive* face, I'm *sure* it's repulsive, however to go back, you *may* remember that *years* ago Haddock brought in the old Divorce Bill, and *one* of the clauses he added on his own was to *abolish* this puerile and fatiguing *nisi*-nonsense, which *by* the way it seems they do *not* have in Bonny *Scotland*, I mean there you're divorced or *not* and no doubt about it, where*as* of course for *six* months my *hunted* Iodine is neither one thing *nor* the other, she's *no* husband but she can't *marry*, which is *against* nature and practically *everything*, well to go back *that* clause was *whisked* out at once in Committee, because they said the *King's* Proctor *must* have the six months to probe about for *collusion*, etc., and smell out any *unveracities* or half-lies that may have slipped past the *Judge*, I *should* say *by* the way darling that according to Haddock the King's Proctor is a *lovable* variety and his charm-and-merit group is definitely *high*, well but *then* they said that *as* the law stood the Judge *might* grant a decree *unless* he had any reason to suppose that there was any *collusion* or lying or what-not about, I *think* it's Section 178 of something, so they said it was *too* feasible for the plausible and low-intention type to slip a wicked one past the poor Judge while he wasn't looking, *hence* they said the Decree *Nisi* in 1860 and *hence* how *indispensable* still the Decree *Nisi* in 1937, my dear have you the *faintest* notion what all this is about, *just* read it over and over again darling *quite* slowly, because honestly my dear Haddock says there are *quite* scores of *thousands* of citizens in the same *crazy* quandary as our Iodine today.

Well of course it seems worn down by all this *ponderous* metal poor Haddock had to surrender his little clause and the old Bill *trundled* along, but my dear *this* is the stagger, *what* happened *next*, why my dear they said we *can't* have collusion and everything and *what's* more we *won't* have our judges *deceived*, so they altered section 178 of what-was-it and turned it round the other way, so that *now* my dear it says the judge *shall not* grant a decree *at all* unless he's *too* satisfied there's *no* collusion, lying, etc., my dear if he's the *least* suspicion he must say *No*, you *do* see the point now *don't* you darling, because it means that *if* he's a good judge which one *must* assume darling he *can't possibly* have been *deceived*, whereas you still have this barbarous *nisi*-stuff the *whole* point of which is that he may have been deceived *still*, and of course Haddock says the *nisi*-law is absolutely a *concrete* insult to His Majesty's Judgery.

However *so* much for the law darling, *now* for the gruesome *events*, well my dear the *first* thing was that I get an *appealing* telephone from *tormented* Iodine who is alone in the ancestral villa with her Decree *Unless* and her faithful Nanny, and it seems that *quite* suddenly a policeman appears at the *back* door and asks the petrified Nanny the *most* mild but *intimate* questions about the Iodine Way of Life so to speak, I mean *how* late to bed, *any* men about and *so* forth, well in the *midst* of the narrative there's a *hair*-curling *scream*, because it seems Nanny has just reported there's a *hooded man* at the *front* door, well of course I at once offered the poor waif *sanctuary* in Jill's room who my dear I think now will *never* be demobbed or *anything*, I forget if I told you she's a *Leading* Torpedo *Wren* and knows *quite* everything about Volts and Wattery, besides my dear doing *land*-work and massage in the early stages, the *things* they're up to the Youth Movement nowadays, well to return to Iodine and my *Christian* behaviour, because my dear *wet* paint everywhere and Haddock I *rather* think is *rather* attracted, though of course it's too true that he has a *technical* interest, because you know in *this* Parliament he *tried* to introduce *eleven* Bills, *too* numerous and *quite* fruitless because this *inflated* Government has taken *all* the time for their *verbose* megalo*manias*, anyhow *one* of the Bills was to *again* abolish this infantile Decree *Unless*, so one can't complain of a *certain* interest, though *when* it comes to striking *utter* strangers at the *front* door, however I haven't told you all, in fact I *can't*, the thing's an *enigma*, my dear *one* theory is that *someone's* written the King's Proctor an *anonymous* letter about the innocent *Iodine*, which it seems is the done thing in this *indecent* world, and *hence* the *policeman*, but then *who* is the *hatted* man who merely *haunts* the premises, *glues* himself to that lamp-post for absolute *hours* and from time to time *darts* across the road, *hammers* on the front door and *at* once vanishes, *except* as I say my dear when Haddock *biffed* him, well the Haddock hypothesis is that he *is* actually the *respondent* Mr Iodine, because Iodine once thought that she recognized the *walk*, though now of course she's *too* tremulous to even *peep* from a window, that it was *Mr* Iodine who wrote the anonymous letter, to *secure* the policeman, and now does the hooded-man act to keep him *interested*, well of course it all sounds *absolute* bats, but then as Haddock says the Decree *Unless is* absolute bats, and of course it seems that *Mr* Iodine *is* actually that sort of *type*, so there's *no* reason why *quite* anything should *not* occur, and of course the hooded man may *well* be a *detective*, but my dear the drab thing is that Iodine has three months to go at *least*, so *what* will happen in *this* poor home, and if anyone defends these *flatulent* laws, but of course *all* the King's Ministers think about is *nationalizing* this and that, *Oh* dear, farewell your agitated TOPSY.

LETTER VII

SAVING AT THE RACES

November 21, 1945.

Trix darling of *course* we'll turn every *stone* about your Maria Whatisitska, but Haddock says you must tell *more*, my dear what *is* she, you say *go* to the Russian Embassy, but my deluded rustic there *is* no Russian Embassy, at least not in the London Telephone Book, there's a *Soviet* Embassy merely, where Haddock says they speak the Soviet language, and of course if she's *Soviet* it seems she might be Georgian, Kamchatkan, Ukrainian, or even Russian, but then again from what you say she might be an *Estonian* or Lithuanian, and in *that* case who knows what, because it seems *nobody* quite knows if *they're* Soviet or not, anyhow there *is* an Estonian Legation in the TB and a Lithuanian *likewise*, so perhaps that would be the better avenue, it's *too* confusing, and by the way Haddock says you mustn't talk about a Soviet *national* because that at least can mean *quite* nothing, however darling we'll do our best.

Well, my dear we've just had a rather *jeopardous* adventure, *too* nerve-removing, I must explain that *poor* Haddock like other pubs, and when I say *pubs* darling I of course mean public *men*, not houses, my dear I do think there ought to be an absolute *statue* somewhere to *all* the pubs of England, when you *think* of all the fraying toil they undertake for *quite* nothing, I *definitely* can not envisage *why*, and of course the more you do for nothing the more the *entire* population seems to think that you've *nothing* to do but to do things for *nothing*, I mean go weakly onto *one* Committee and *half* the Committees in the kingdom swarm upon you, my dear we know men who spend all their *days* in Committee, whether it's Water Boards or *Catchment* Areas or *Saving* Europe or *Improving* Prisons, and my dear getting *quite* nothing out of it but *national* umbrage and premature tuberculosis, my dear Haddock says he knows *three* men who are *quite* never out of the *Chair*, as for Mr H himself who is a mere *amateur* and short-time pub, well in the old days he never *deigned* to *lecture* except too haughtily for a mass of *guineas*, not that he has the *smallest* urge or even *theme* to lecture about *anyhow*, but now that he's a semi-reluctant pub there is not *one* Society, Gov. Department or *Youth* Movement that does not it seems expect him to lecture for nothing *quite all the time*, my dear the letters cascade in daylong, my dear it takes days to say *No* to half of them, not to mention the *lethal* expenditure on stamps, Haddock has a Movement for a *Sixpenny* Post, and *how* the old overdraft is to be equilibrized is *not* it seems a problem that is taken *too* seriously anywhere outside *this* humble home, however *as* I was saying like the other pubs *poor* Mr H from time to time is cajoled and goaded to speak at a *Savings* Week meeting and from time to time does so because it's the *done* thing, which of course is *so* spurious because my dear *try* how we may we do *not* seem to save a *shekel* and one can *hear* poor Mr H's conscience kicking while he *implores* the charwomen to give up their yachting and oysters and invest their all in these *drab* certificates, besides which I am *not* positive that he knows *much* more than I do about *inflation* and everything, which is *about* ZERO minus 14, anyhow I notice there's rather a *skating* movement when such topics are touched upon, however the *key*-point of this narrative approaches *now*, which is that as you *may* or may not remember for *quite* years he's been *going on* about the taxation of *betting*, which does not *exist*, and of course *now* he says *how* incompatible it is all this *Purchase* Tax on everything you *buy*, all this *murderous* mulcting of everything you *earn*, and all this *pontifical* yap about *saving*, when my dear if you put a *hundred* Peppiatts on some *ludicrous* horse you pay *no tax at all*, not even if it *rattles* home at 50 to 1 and you win a great *wad* of Peppiatts, which one *has* to agree darling has a *tinge* of *plausibility*, well anyhow *being* invited to address the *Chamber* of Commerce and the *massed* Rotarians of Burbleton about saving he said what *is* the purpose, *all* those respectables will do the old duty *anyhow*, why if I *must* utter not utter on the *racecourse* where I see the Autumn Gathering will be proceeding, the *Big Race* is on the identical day, and the untutored proletariat will be *squandering* their hard-earned on *anti-social* and go-slow *horses*.

Well darling *somewhat* to my surprise and apprehension it *was* so, my dear we were parked in the *Silver* Ring or somewhere, *too* close to the *loudest* bookies and with a sort of lectern-arrangement like theirs, only of course instead of the *odds* and so forth *our* blackboard was all about these dreary *certificates*, well my dear Mr H opened fire between the 2.50 and the *Big* Race, with an audience of *about* one man, as a matter of fact I didn't hear *all* his opening speech because I *slipped* away to put a fiver on Love Lies *Bleeding*, which Frank told me could *not* be beaten, and ten bob each way on Diadem for Frank's Nanny, rather a *melting* bookie my dear called *Oats*, and I *rather* think he was *rather* attracted, we still have *remnants* of the old charm darling, however he said *What's* the old bloke belly-aching about lady, which being a reference to my only husband I explained the *Savings* Message *briefly* with the *result* my dear that Mr Oats went *quite* purple and began yelling *Ten* to one the *Field don't* forget the Old Firm lady *Come* to us and you'll have something to *save*, in which I must say I did see the *point* don't you, so then I went back to Haddock who *stung* and galvanized was shouting madly about *certificates* and two and a half per *cent*, which *works* out I gather my dear at about *two* to

one after eight years, and the cries of *ten* to one the field and
100 to 8 Diadem did somehow have a more convincing *ring*,
well by this time a rather *acidulous* little crowd had massed
round Haddock, my dear some *quite* unChristian and muscular
categories, as a matter of fact I *might* have heard my bonhomous
Mr Oats say something about Handle him lad to one of his own
henchmen, who had a face my dear *exactly* like a whale's ear,
anyhow it was *too* clear that the *sense* of the audience was not
utterly with Haddock, *things* were being audibly said *quite* alien
to the Savings Movement, I mean when Haddock got to
inflation and everything a man would sing out *Forty* to one
Inflation, or Six to four on *Thrift*, *too* out of keeping, and one
man shouted Send for the *police*, which I thought was a *little*
harsh on the envoy of the State, well presently there was a
rather *pointed* little rush towards the lectern, so of course *all* the
motherbird in me rose up at once, I *sprang* to the side of my
poor threatened pub and began a private yell of my *own*, my
dear I can *not* record all the things I said to those citizens, my
dear Parasitical *louts* was about the most *unprovocative* of all my
assertions, and of course the *laughable* thing was that suddenly
I found I was *too* serious about the *entire* Savings Movement, my
dear if you could have *seen* those *uncivic* creatures with their
wads of Peppiatts and greedy eyes, and my dear the *entire*
paraphernalia of horsery is *so* pseudo when you come to think
of it, my dear not *one* of those avaricious *sportmen* had ever
touched a horse I *swear*, and of course the *other* laugh was that
whatever I said about their antecedents and *obscene* appearance
I *rather* think they were *rather* attracted, indeed Haddock says
that with the little eyes flashing and everything, and I'd got on
my new blue two-piece, *18* coupons, the old form was definitely
recaptured, anyhow they were as mute as newts, and fortunately
the *Big* Race beginning they dispersed at last with a few rude
cries of *Forty* to one Inflation, well *then* my dear to *crown* all as
perhaps you remember my *adored* Love Lies Bleeding came in
quite first, with Diadem a good *second*, so in rather an *astringent*

33

silence I collected *fifty* Peppiatts from the unamused Mr Oats, who said sultrily Mind you *save* it lady, and as a matter of fact I have bought *three* or four of Haddock's *insipid* certificates, which is more than Haddock has, so all's well, etcetera, but what a *day*, farewell your battling TOPSY.

LETTER VIII

THE DANES

November 28, 1945.

Trix, darling, *where* am I, I'll give you *four* guesses, *right* in the middle of the *Kiel* Canal on the darkest night in the *most* appealing *butter*-boat bringing butter and eggs and *bacon* from the Danes to *England*, because my dear Haddock's been *lecturing* in Copenhagen, it's still not utterly manifest *why*, but concerning that you must ask the British Council and everything and when I say lecturing he merely rises *without* notes and burbles bonhomously for *quite* hours, which I must say the Danes did seem to suffer *gladly*, but then of course they are the *completest* pets with *angels'* manners and a British sense of humour, my dear the *shaming* thing is that they contrive to *laugh* at Haddock's most *esotteric* anecdotes, and of course why on earth that *overrated* author made that *bilious* citizen Hamlet a Dane is *quite* inexplicable, most of them talk English *far* better than the English and many of them you'd bet *six* pairs of fully-fashioneds that they were *native* Brits, whereas of course Haddock and I can say *quite* nothing in their tongue except *Skaal* which is Cheer-O and *Tak* which is Ta duckie, and those of course you say *all* day, my dear Haddock has just *startlingly* refused a Schnapps at 0900, the children *all* acquire English it seems, my dear *one* morning at 0400 we were woken up by *small* boys vociferating *Tipperary* with which odious ditty they

35

used to madden the Germans one gathers, and my dear *how* they abominate the Germans, well *can* you wonder, not only Tipperary they know *all* the island anthems, my dear at the 60*th* anniversary of the *English* Debating Club which was the just cause and excuse for the Haddock sortie, my dear the *drill* is that *at* the meetings not *one* word of Danish is uttered and when you think that for *sixty* years all this has been proceeding it *is* a little wonder-worthy and pride-producing you *must* admit, well my dear Haddock had brought a *genial* message from the Speaker and the *entire* company *about* five hundred arose and *stood* while he read it, *too* stirring, and then at the supper they sang *Auld* Lang Syne and *He's* a Jolly Good, and my dear Haddock *not* content with having orated for one *complete* hour must *now* be upstanding and sing his *Beveridge* song, Oh *won't* it be wonderful after the *war*, which personally I thought was *rather* unprovoked and even out of *keeping*, however my *gorgeous* Danes digested the ditty *at* once and it's now *practically* the new national *hymn*, because my dear the next night at the Students' Union at the *University* where Haddock gave another *inexcusably* protracted discourse about parliaments and everything, my *dear* how I suffered and as a *matter* of fact about *half*-way through I *rather* thought the old man himself would sink into a *stupor*, and *actually* as it turned out he *was* sickening for a *food*-fever which is what *all* the English become a casualty to it seems after about five days of this *enchanting* Danish *alimentation*, well anyhow at the end of *questions*, which I thought were a shade shy and sparkless on the part of the Youth Movement, but then can you *wonder* in an alien *tongue*, well then a far from unmagnetic *froken* petitions Haddock to sing his *Beveridge* which they've read about in the morning it seems, *after* which my dear they all sing *everything* from My *Bonny* is Over to *Loch* Lomond, A *Tavern* in a Town, *Annie* Laurie and The Prettiest Girl I ever Saw sat sucking Cyder through a *Straw*, the last being another *quite* superfluous Haddock solo, well my dear if you could have *heard* those young you'd have sworn it was a bunch of Brits, *no* accent and *what* spirit, *quite* electrical, well we wound up with Auld Langers and the Danish National, and the same day Haddock had a *princely* lunch with a *platoon* of lawyers who he says discussed the most *obtruse* points of English law in *top* English, and this morning my dear while I'm watching one of the seamen burning paint with a *blow*-lamp *what* is the *first* thing he starts to whistle, When Irish Eyes are *Smiling*, so altogether as Haddock says *if* there *is* going to be a Western *block* or something there could *not* be a *much* better foundation than the Danes, because my dear *after* all the whole Prussian filthery did begin in 1864 it seems, when Denmark was the first unlucky virgin so to speak, and my dear in the *late* conflict I do *not* think one *quite* recalls just *how* tough and unfraternal the Danes were to the septic *Germans*, for one thing as Haddock said in a speech *uncongenial* though bombs may be one does remember saying *constantly* in the blitz-days and doodletimes Well anyhow this is no great *fun* but *how* much worse to have *Germans* about the place, better *two* incendiaries on the roof than one Prussian at the front-*door*, and my dear I can *not* envisage *how* we could have *endured* to see that *contagious* and inflated race *strutting* about the Strand and *swilling* at the Savoy and so forth, well my dear the Danes it seems merely *wore* the vermin *away*, always *too* polite one gathers when they weren't blowing up railways or their own *pet* buildings, or else making the *rudest* jokes, my dear I *adore* the bookseller who put pictures of Hitler and the *Top* Wop in his window and *in* between them the *largest* copy of *Les Misérables*, poor sweet incarcerated of *course*, and my dear *ab initio* there were *Churchill* Clubs in *half* the High Schools, and in 1940 during the Battle of B. *three* quarters of a million Danes it seems came out *quite* suddenly into the streets and parks and everywhere and *sang*, merely *sang*, they called it an *All*-Sing, just to *show* the cosmos, which of course the Germans thought was *too* out of place, and *how* I *ache* to have seen their *superb* King Christian *horse*-riding about the streets in the early morning *quite* unaccompanied, *that* is till the Huns interned him, and then of course when the Jew-nonsense began and they said that all the Jews were to wear the *Yellow* Star, the King said in this country there is *no* Jew-problem for we have never considered ourselves *inferior* to the Jews, and as for this Star-stuff the King and the *entire* Court will wear the Yellow Star *likewise*, so *that* was a flop, my dear what *can* you do with such people, well then in '43 of course they *all* blew up, King, Parliament *and* Populace, they said they were *too* congested with the German race and it could transfer itself to any *appropriate* place as long as it was *quite* elsewhere, well *then* the afflicted Huns had to *invade* the Model Protectorate *again*, the police were turned out, there was sabotage and *anti*-sabotage, because wherever the Danes blew up a *factory* the Huns blew up some favourite place like a Yacht Club or cinema, my dear *too* infantile, and *by* the way you *ought* to see the *Shell* building where the obscene Gestapo gang resided, right in the *heart*, I mean about Trafalgar *Square*, and the RAF came over and *quite* obliterated the lair, *three* minutes before the sirens went, and 200 of the vermin slain, *what* a job, the Danes will *never* forget it, well then there were strikes and *more* strikes, and the Huns decreed a *curfew* at 8 o'clock, my dear in *summer* time, so *what* do you think the Danes came out in the streets and lit the largest *bonfires*, well in the *end* it seems the Germans saw *three* red lights and utterly agreed to *terms*, *no* curfew and who knows *what*, so that will show you what *can* be done by a bijou St George with *top*-guts and no sword at *all*, and as a matter of fact they say if the conflict had continued *much* they'd have had *all* the co-operative *dairies* striking and then the poor Prussians would have had no *butter*.

Well here we are in this almost *invisible* steamer, the dear little *Rota*, my dear Haddock says she's *just* over 1000 tons but swift and *quite* full of bacon and butter for you and yours, the captain by the way who is the *ocean's* darling and I *rather* think is *rather* attracted, was deep in the underground stuff *throughout* the conflict, my dear *smuggling* Danes and our parachute chaps across to Norway and everything, one time he says he had *30* chaps behind the cargo with the Germans ramping about the hold, however I must close now because we're approaching the *ocean* end of the said Canal, the captain says the wind is Force 5 in the North Sea which Haddock says is *quite* enough if not more, so I propose creeping into the *bottom* bunk *forthwith*, a pity my dear because I was *eager* to tell you about the *food* at Copenhagen, the cooking in this ship by the way is a thing to *sing* about and last night we went on a *Skaaling* party round Aalborg with this *magnetic* captain, beginning my dear with sherry *and* port in an antique cellar, proceeding to a *unique* old tavern with schnapps and *beer*, followed by a sumptious dinner with the celebrated Danish cherry *brandy*, fortunately there's *no* skaaling once we leave port so there *has* been a day of rest, but whether the little frame is *quite* attuned to Force 5 in the North Sea is something that remains to be *proved*, farewell, your faintly unconfident TOPSY.

LETTER IX

FORCE 5

November 29, 1945.

Well Trix darling, we've *issued* from the Kiel Canal at *last*, and now after two days we're in the *North* Sea and *practically* on our way to London, though even now we have to go right up to the *Humber* and then down the *coast* it seems because of *mines*, but then as Haddock says what *does* it matter, my dear I do think he's *so* right about the *overrated* Air, well of course if we'd aviated we'd have been back in four hours, we took *five* coming because of adverse tempests, but my dear *what* hours, that *dreary* noise the entire time, you *can't* move, you *can't* read, you've *no* idea where you are, and as for feeling you're monarch of the air you feel more like a *deaf* prisoner in a third-class dungeon bumping up and down in an *insufferable* din, my dear you can *see* nothing, coming over I had the *minutest* window *thick* with rain through *which* you could see about four clouds and the starboard *wing*, and if there *is* any object more boring than an aircraft's wing, *added* to which of course you see no *life*, I mean you can *roar* over Denmark, Holland *and* Germany and know no more about the people than if they were *fishes*, whereas in *this* way pottering about by ship and puff-puff, of course we've had the craziest journey because to get from Copenhagen to Kiel we first travelled *west* in a ship all night, then *north* for four hours in a train, then *south* again for a day

40

and a night in *this* bijou vessel, *nearly* my dear getting back to Copenhagen, which sounds *too* wrong to the speed-fiends and save-timers, on the other hand *all* the time we've been seeing *Danes*, and *Jutland*, and the farms and railways, and the wrecks in the Baltic which are *quite* phenomenal, my dear the Captain says the ships are *still* going skyward where we were last *night*, then of course there was that *electric* skaaling-party at Aalborg to which no aeroplane could *ever* get you, and Kiel Harbour, what with the *fat* battleships *quite* upside down and the Hun pilot being polite to the Danes at *last*, and the *rather* compelling British naval officer in his *German* launch with a *German* crew and a *German* officer gold-cap and all, *too* satisfying darling, well as Haddock says *how* much of *all* this do you see with a bird's-eye *view*, not *much*.

On the *other* hand of course we may still stimulate a *mine* or two, and your little friend can no longer conceal from herself that we are *pretty* definitely at *sea*, because whether the wind is Force 3 or Force *13* the undulation is quite *noticeable*, my dear don't think I'm *nauseous* or anything, it's only the faintest apprehension of *unease*, if you know what I mean, and perhaps the *sage* thing will be to lie still and tell you more about *Copenhagen* to keep the *mind* off the dubious tummy, well darling Copenhagen I *rather* feel is *almost* my favourite city, of course I've not seen Stockholm about which they all talk ravingly, there are the *most* arresting buildings everywhere with *quantities* of the tallest spires and things, most of them in *lizard* green, which they say is because it's *copper* I can *not* envisage *why*, my dear Haddock has just been in and he says the wind is only Force *4* South Easterly but *freshening*, the drab thing will be if I miss the mid-day *meal*, I think there's a dim hope still because my delicious Danes do everything at the *wrongest* time, my dear we *lunch* at 11.30 and have dinner at half-past-*five* which gives one *rather* a protracted evening, but my dear *what* meals, the entire crew is only 21, but you couldn't *comb* Soho for more salubrious cooking and the *most* paternal steward, the *overture* to lunch is like *all* the stories, my dear yesterday I counted *fifteen* things on the table and *all* enchanting, there were *two* kinds of smoked herring and one smoked *sole*, with *onions*, imagine darling, *two* categories of bacon no three I think because one was hot, some fascinating sliced *ham*, some sort of hot *fish*, two types of egg-food, *liver* pâté, home made and high marks for succulence, cold pork, and *pressed* beef, sausages in two styles, oh yes and mayonnaise of *salmon* and some sort of *inscrutable* stuff I cannot classify, all this my dear accompanied by schnapps, with *chasers* of refreshing lager, *not* to mention a *mountain* of butter, and of course *just* when you think the meal is over, *not* that you tackle *all* the things of *course*, it's just the *spectacle*, well *in* comes some *hot* pork or beef or somewhat *magically* but *simply* cooked, actually, my dear they do *not* consume excessively but there *is* no doubt they understand the art of *living*, however perhaps one had better *discontinue* this discussion because it's putting ideas into the little *tummy* and it's now *too* manifest that steamers of 1000 tons ought *not* to go about the oceans *excepting* in the *flattest* calm, my dear Haddock who's *indecently* well keeps *surging* in and saying *What* a good *sea-boat* which I've told him not to say again, however to go back to the buildings which *may* be safer, there's one fantastic pale-green spire made of the tails of *four* dragons *twisted* together, I'll send you a postcard and as for the *Radio* House which we went *all* over after Haddock's broadjaw, it's *too* palacious, *Greenland* granite and the *most* beautiful Concert Hall you ever saw, altogether my dear it makes the poor old BBC look like a suburban *pub*, they say they had to *bribe* the German anti-sabotagers not to blow the whole thing heavenward, my dear Haddock has been in again *encrusted* with brine, he says the wind is now definitely Force 5 and *backing*, lunch is on the table and there are two *new* categories of smoked herring and *cured* bacon, but my dear I grieve to say it but I *seem* to have lost *all* interest in *bacon*, I've consented feebly to a small hot *soup* and perhaps if I continue to keep the mind

42

on *you*, well the *shops*, my dear at *that* moment there was a shattering *thump* and the ship did actually stand on its *head*, *quite* all the clothes flew off and the little feet pattered against the bunk *above*, *too* alarming I'm *not* sure but I should think it was a *mine*, no Haddock has since transpired with the soup and *all* he said was *What* a good *sea-boat*, well the shops, my dear I could *not* get any chocolate for you because that's rationed and there are absolute *queues*, butter's rationed too but seems to be prolific by our standards, there's *no* tea, and they ache for tobacco and coffee, my dear an English *cigarette* is practically *manna*, a shilling for one was the done thing recently, then of course there are *no* hot baths because of no coal, which is a fraying detail maybe but affects a girl's life as *you* know, and I mention all this, my dear the soup has cascaded *all* over my night-wear, because I *don't* want you to think that my darling Danes are living *heartlessly* in the lap of lux, far from it, they're doing all they can to do the Christian thing, well *meat* is in *masses*, my dear if you could *see* the butchers' shops, *enormous* cattle and festoons of oxtails, but they can't distribute more it seems because of *transport*, meanwhile as Haddock says it *is* a comfort to see *one* corner of *civilization* surviving, I mean in the way of *eating*, le manger, there are the *most* atmospheric old restaurants and oak taverns, and personally, I should *hate* to see them reduced to *our* abyssmal queueing and scraping, because *after* all it is an *Art*, which ought to be preserved and fostered, my dear the fried sole at our hotel was a *dream*, and as for the *cheese*, my dear the *Roquefort*, oh gosh such thoughts are a fraction *dangerous*, and of course *when* they give you a *special* lunch to show you what the old times were it actually *is* a spiritual *experience*, so is the *skaaling*, Haddock asserts the wind is *abating* but it's not *too* perceptible *here*, my dear there's none of our *casual* sipping and swilling, every drink is a *solemn* toast, you look *deep* and earnest into *all* the eyes and say *Skaal*, then you *bow*, my dear it's more like a religious *ritual*, which again is a sign of *civilization*, well *can* you envisage some of our gin-groups behaving thuswise, however, they're *so* hospitable that to an untrained British tummy the task is *formidable*, and I must say that after *six* days my pathetic Haddock had a pain in the *midriff* which he described untactfully as a *duodanal* ulcer, however it wasn't and *today* as I think I said he's odiously well, he's just announced my dear that we've passed the P10 *buoy* and we've only another *three hundred* and fifty miles to go, the *wind* is freshening again and *drawing* ahead, my dear he also described the whole of his *disgusting* lunch as a result of which my dear I rather fancy the *worst* is about to

It did darling, farewell your suffering TOPSY.

LETTER X

THE NEW HOUSE

December 6, 1945.

Trix darling, I grovel about the pencil, *not* to mention the *squalid* paper, and I shouldn't wonder if this actual *letter* turned out a shade miscellaneous and disordinated, when I tell you where I *am*, my dear I'm waiting in the *Central* Hall at the House while Haddock seeks a seat in the Gallery for me, which I gather is *practically* prohibitive, my dear you've *no* conception of the *multitudinous* conditions in this place now, it is *actually* the National Home for *Queues*, because you know for *years* past the populace have sniffed and snooted at the *whole* institution, it was the *gasworks* and the *talking*-shop and such, and every Member was a septic *politician*, my dear the *meanest* category of personnel, in fact during the late conflict as Haddock used to say, it *sometimes* sounded as if the Populace had *no* use for what they were *fighting* for, if you see what I mean, however now that the Populace have swamped the polls all's well it seems, *too* erroneous of course but satis*fac*tory, my dear there's a *sedentary* queue of constituents *all* down St Stephen's Hall which is *exactly* like a *refrigerator* except for statues of Burke and Pitt and even they have small *calory* value, sometimes Haddock says the queue *expands* standing into the street outside, *all* this my dear to hear the whifflings of the *septic* politician in the gashouse or *talking*-shop, *too* as it should be but not unlaughworthy, while in the *Chamber* it seems the Members have to *queue* up to the Sergeant-at-Arms, or should that be spelt with a j, I believe it's the done thing, with the same weird purpose, and as for where I am, my dear it's like *market*-day at Burbleton or Bunbury, I haven't seen any *cows* but *quite* congested, you can't *move* for all these *herds* of electors waiting to extract their Members with *Green* Cards and humble petitions, *rather* stirring as Haddock says because it shows the *interest* but a *shade* fraying for the battered *Members*, because of course it may be the *one* debate they ought to hear and instead they have to hither-and-thither for tickets or tea, *during* which somebody in the Chamber is saying *carbolically I*'m *surprised* not to see the Hon. Member in his *place* and so forth, and by the way Haddock says the amount of *superfluous* carbolic about is *too* synthetic and boring, my dear you know how they always say that the start of a new Parliament is *exactly* like a new term at a Public school, well my dear he showed me one of the *Members'* telephone boxes where *two* days after the opening someone had written on the wall in *block* letters 200 TORIES CAN'T BE RIGHT, at which he thought Well the new term is starting with a bang, but my dear the *next* day it seems someone had rubbed out the T in CAN'T SO that it *now* read 200 TORIES CAN, *etc.*, and the *next* day the T was back again, the last thing was that someone wrote rather pompously underneath it, *Please* see notice about defacing *walls*, then someone scratched the whole saga out, *too* adolescent don't you think, however so far Haddock says there've been *no* rude pictures or hearts with arrows through them *yet*, though some fiery fellow did draw a hammer and sickle in the dust over one of the lavs, but that perhaps was some volcanic *visitor*, and *by* the way I don't think I *ever* told you about the *one* disconcertment we had in Copenhagen, my dear after Haddock had been interviewed by *quite* all the papers who were *too* nice and non-violent, he happened to see in one of them a column with a heading which *looked* like Stories about *Haddock*, *too* right, because my dear a friendly Dane interpreting it seems they'd attributed to my *blameless* Haddock three or four of those *antique* practical *joke* stories about the *renowned* practical joker Horace somebody I can *not* recall his name, my dear it was Haddock we understand they said who dug the *largest* hole in Whitehall and was a pest to the traffic for *simply* days *pretending* my dear to be someone from the gas or Water Board, likewise it was *Haddock* we believe who gave his stop-watch to Sir *John* Simon, challenged him to run down a piece of Piccadilly in so many seconds and *when* he had started yelled *Stop* thief he's got my *watch*, my dear *John* Simon of all people *can* you imagine it, and can you *conceive* our blushes, because my dear if there *is* a thing my sunny spouse has *never* done it's practical *jokery*, *too* infantile we've *always* thought, and *now* my dear in a strange city on a *goodwill* mission, my dear we *scarcely* dared to emerge at *all* for fear the *police* would be watching us, though of course in the late conflict there was *no* sort of *practical* mockery the Danes did *not* do to the septic *Germans*, my dear one man put an advertisement in the paper *Quantities* of second-hand furniture to sell *Ring* number so-and-so, the said number being the telenumber of the *Gestapo*, who my dear went *utterly* bats answering applications for *beds* and wardrobes and could *not* ring Hitler or anyone up for *days*, so it may be they thought that Haddock's alleged antics were part of a *Resistance* Movement and took a Christian view.

Well, here I am still, darling and *no* Haddock, a lonely cork on the animated sea, but my dear I could sit here for *days* it's *so* human, my dear the *pathetic* constituents whose Members are *not* here, or can't come out perhaps, my dear like *dogs* waiting for the front door to open, *too* forlorn, and then of course the *Members* hither-and-thithering *manfully* my dear with that sort of *destiny* air they *all* have, bless them, as if D Day might be *any* minute, the dank thing is that nowadays I know so *few* of them, and *snooping* down at us of course those appealing little *stone* kings and queens on *all* the walls, talking of snooping my dear

I've just given rather a *glacial* grin to Mr *Ferret*, I'll tell you later perhaps, however *what* I was saying was that *after* all I *am* sitting in the absolute *bosom* of the Mother of P's, *half*-way between the Lords and Commons, and *just* where the People come to meet the *Parliament*, my dear through the door I can *just* see Mr Pitt at the *other* end of St Stephen's Hall and opposite him is the enormous Mr Fox, *too* alarming, and my dear it *is* rather moving to think that that is *exactly* where they used to jaw and jangle in the aged days, when it was Pitt not Winston, though of course I definitely can *not* envisage that they had *half* the coping to do that we have, my dear have you the *faintest* notion what *Burnham Woods* is about, and then this *quite* inscrutable *Loan*, Haddock says he *rather* thinks that he may vote *against* it because it's the one thing that may stop him *smoking* at last and he could hardly care less if there were no more *films*, though I dare say there *is* a little more in it than *that*, my dear there's that Mr Ferret again who Haddock thinks *may* be one of the *pseudo-squad*, it seems that some of the Members have taken to writing articles about this place in the bilious weeklies under *false* names, my dear *too* pompous and *inflated* names like *Judex*, *Liberator* or Titus *Oates*, and some of them say the most *corrosive* things about the other Members, which Haddock thinks *if* it's the done thing it's time it *wasn't*, because he says *however* hot the argy-bargy in the Chamber the done thing is to be fair and frank *outside*, and even *in*, well I mean on the whole you don't chew up a chap who's not *there*, and anyhow it's all *quite* public, so the other chap can bang you *back* perhaps, next time, moreover after a banging-match you can *always* meet over a noggin in the Smoking-room and bang it out again in friendly fashion, when of course you *may* remember all the things you *forgot* to say before and so forth, which in the old days he says led to *many* amiable battles between the incompatibles, whereas now it seems you may be standing a chap a *double* whisky tonight when *last* week he called you a *vested* interest a reactionary what-not or Fascist *lackey*, *not* he says that *that* would matter if only you *knew*, because then you could buy him *another* whisky and matily explain just *where* he was *erroneous*, though personally I should save my Scotch for someone who had *not* called me a vested interest or *even* a reactionary *what-not*, but that I know is *not* the Commons way of life, and I must say there *may* be something in what Haddock says because here I am in a *dubious* state about poor Mr Ferret, who may *not* be one of the pseudo-squad at *all*, and at one time I *rather* thought that he was *rather* attracted, oh dear, here's Haddock at last, farewell your devoted TOPSY.

LETTER XI

THE PRIME MERIDIAN

December 13, 1945.

Trix darling, one hundred salvoes from a thousand *guns*, this is my *Christmas* epistle to the frozen *North*girls, I don't suppose for a moment you'll get it before *Easter* because of course of the Chriſtmas *rush*, and I won't swear that the *news* in it will be utterly *topical*, because my dear I *did* think *this* year the *septic* Germans being *practically* defeated I *might* have sent you a really *red-hot* Christmas epistle on what the papers call *hard news*, bless them, but my dear *last* night, *did* you hear it, *what* was my dismay and deflation, there was the *most* unencouraging broadjaw from somebody about the *Yuletide* drill, and it said for *pity's* sake don't send any letter after the *August* Bank Holiday, *only* telephone after Whitsun, and *never* telegraph *at all*, as for Christmas greetings on gilded wires, *nothing* it said could be *more* anti-social and everything, and *now* my dear they tell me there are the *largest* GPO vans traversing London today saying TELEPHONE LESS and *never* TELEGRAPH, which my dear is like the *Savoy* putting streamers out to say *don't* COME IN HERE, of course my dear I *know* you'll say all this is *obese* exaggeration, which perhaps it is but *not* much, because my dear that is the absolute *trend* today, I mean the *State* saying we *must* do everything but *don't* expect *me* to do a thing, and the private fellow saying I *ache* to do everything but nobody *lets* me,

50

the *result* of which my dear is *primordial* chaos, and here I am composing my *Chritmas* epistle to you in *mid*-Autumn, and *quite* unable to tell you *what* happened about Burnham Woods and everything, because I'm posting on Friday morning in the dim hope of reaching you before the *first bluebell*, my dear *don't* think for a *moment* that I'm not *completely* ethical about the post-personnel and *telecommunicationmongers*, because *actually* I'd like everyone to have *six* days off before Christmas, *and* another six *after*, my dear *no* food or posts or *gas* or electricity or *anything*, which Haddock thinks is a *shade* unfeasible though *I* should have said *quite* Christmassy in *spirit*, however *there* it is I can *not* tell you *what* happened about Burbleton Woods and everything because it will *not* have happened until after I caught the post tomorrow, if you see what I mean, which of course Haddock says he is *all for* because he says the *stark* menace to humanity is *easy communications*, and the more the State takes over everything the *less* there'll be of *that*, so to speak, well I mean he says after *about* three centuries the State has worked up to *twopence-halfpenny* on a letter from the Strand to *Fleet* Street, and he says with *all-party* support in a year or two they *may* get it up to *sixpence* or more, besides of course *practically* putting a stop to *all telecommunications*, my *dear* what a word, whereas of course if you put some *frightful* wizard like Woolton in charge you'd have letters *whizzing* in at a penny a time, everybody would get through to everyone *at once* and life on the whole would be *too* communicative and unendurable, for which I *must* say there *is* something to be said, don't you agree darling, and I rather hope they'll internationalize the *cosmic* wireless and save us from some of this defatigating *news*.

On the other hand, I do confess, Haddock does have qualms about the Prime *Meridian*, of course my poor rustic I don't suppose you've ever *thought* about the Prime Meridian, and I can't say it's *frequently* kept your little friend awake, but *actually* Haddock says the *Prime* Meridian is Longitude Nought, the merest *line* my dear it seems but it goes through *Greenwich*, in the South-East of *London*, well it seems for *years* and more they've been arranging all the navigation and the *Time* and everything by their laughable line which goes through *Greenwich* of all places, my dear if you'd ever *been* there you'd see what I mean, *not* I gather that there's been the *wee-est* trouble about it, in fact Haddock says the simple *mariners* and birdmen have quite a *feeling* for the place, but there it is it's *too* uncentral and bombed to bits besides of course being about a *year's* tramride from Westminster and everything, *apart* from which of course the whole thing dates a bit from the bad old *Tory* days, and what with one thing and another they appointed the *most* ponderous Committee, which said that Greenwich was *too* unsuitable and far away, and to *mark* the New Era the *Prime* Meridian ought to be moved to *Westminster*, and pass *if* possible through the *County Hall* in memory of Herbert *Morrison*, well darling *rustic* though you are I *expect* you'll see the point of *that*, but there was the *most* acidulous row in the House, because it seems the astrosophers said they would have to start *all over again*, and how would anyone know where the *Moon* was or anything, to which of course the Gov. replied, It's the New Era and Damureyes, which it seems is the done thing nowadays, and if anyone who *knew* anything *said* anything there was a mocking *yell*, which also is the done thing now, however on a division it passed by a *183*, and that was *that*, but *now* comes the rubble and wife, as the Civil Defence man said, my dear I wonder if you're giving the *faintest* attention to my Christmas message, *if* not *do* read it *all* over again *quite* slowly, because honestly my dear you *must* try to keep *abreast* of civilization, *whatever* Henry does in his woods and spinneys, well you see *now* the *cosmos* had to be consulted, and of course the *cosmos* who never had a *word* to say about *Greenwich*, the moment there was all this yap about *Westminster* the *entire* cosmos began to have *ideas*, as you *may* imagine, well first of all the Dominions, my dear Canada it seems said the Magnetic North, whatever *that* may be, was *practically* at her back-door and *how* suitable, etcetera, and Australia said she was *half*-way between the Old World and the New and the *Prime* Meridian ought to go through *her*, causing Haddock says *practically* Civil War between Melbourne and Sydney, *not* to mention Canberra, well then South Africa said what about *Gold*, so they had a *Conference*, which I believe sits still, *meanwhile* of course the remaining humans were *all* muttering snootily *What* is all this British *Imperialism* and *Why* should the Prime be on British soil *at all*, anywhere, my dear the Portuguese were *too* umbrageous, the Americans said *New* York or nowhere and on the whole *Fifth* Avenue, the Zionists of course had *quite* other notions, my dear the *riots* in Calcutta and *Jerusalem*, and so it went on, *finally* my dear the suffering Russians got wind of it, the new idea, and now of course there's a *cosmic* conference in the pot, the *result* of which Haddock thinks will be that the Prime Meridian will be placed in Sweden, *unless* it moves from place to place at *five*-yearly intervals, *thus* driving *all* the astrosophers and navigators *bats*, which only shows as Haddock says how *sage* it may be to leave *some* things *alone*.

Well darling, I do hope my Christmas message may seed and fructify in your *slough* of a mind, if you'll forgive my poetry, it's not quite snowing, but the house is *thick* with fog, the gas is anaemic, my tiny hands are *frozen*, I *rather* think *all* the pipes will explode tonight, gangsters I'm *quite* confident surround the home, Haddock for all I know is *voting* for Burnham *Woods*, the twins are distant and probably *engaged*, but after all there will *not* be no *sireens* tonight, and *peering* through the fog I seem to see Britannia in the *arms* of Father Christmas, *utterly* illuminated by *rays* of hope, so *all* the happiest my oldest turtle, and for Heaven's sake don't *touch* that cheese if you think it's gone a *yard* too far, farewell, good Yuling, your antiquated TOPSY.

LETTER XII

GOOD RESOLUTIONS

January 1, 1946.

Trix, my little sunspot, I'm *quite* moribund with Christmas are you, my dear the *shopping*, and the *coping*, it's *too* satisfying to think we've got twelve *clear* , months now before we have to go through it again, my dear *could* I get my poor Haddock so much as a new *pipe*, *not* anywhere though I *ransacked* the city, you would think, wouldn't you with all the *trees* we have in the land we could produce a *few* small pieces of wood with holes in them in which tobacco could be burned conveniently, because after all what *is* a pipe, they're made it seems of French briar, but why not *British* briar my dear you have *so* much surplus space up there I suppose you couldn't get Henry to plant a *grove* of briars for Haddock's pipes, Jill could fabricate them when she's demobbed if ever, because there's *quite* nothing she can't do with her hands, she makes the *most* appealing toys for children in the torpedo shed, or somewhere, and as Haddock says, on the other hand of course I need *hardly* say that Haddock has just given up smoking again for *quite* ever, and this time he says it's final because of the *dollar* area or something, nevertheless darling I should go ahead with the *briar-grove* if I were you, talking of *good* resolutions I've been in conference with the better self a good bit recently, and about some things I've made the most *steely* decisions, haven't you, because my dear I do think that *this* year is going to be so *unspeakably* macaber that really one must make an *utter* surrender to the better self and be a sort of *torch* and beacon to those about one, don't you agree darling, the drear thing is it *is* so difficult to get the *practicalities* clear, well for instance you know the new rule is *If* we've got anything we want *export* it, which *may* sound like the signature-tune of a bat to you my dear but *actually* it is political *economy*, and of course every *penny* you spend is the last and fatal step to *inflation*, or perhaps *deflation*, I never *have* known which is which and now I've abandoned the struggle, well of course the very *first* thing I vowed was to utterly *expel* the juniper-juice and everything from my life, *except* after 6 on alternate Saturdays because, my dear I thought if only we *all* did that what *quantities* of gin we could export to America, well then of course Haddock says he thinks we don't export gin very prolificly to America I'm thinking of *whisky*, which I never *touch*, *too* discouraging, however that is *actually* going to be the way of life this year because of *inflation*, and then of course *accounts*, my dear I've bought the *largest* ledger and I'm going to record *quite* every penny and Peppiatt we spend, of course I know there *have* been years that *started* thus before, but *genuinely* this will be *too* different, I'm going to have *two* columns, one for expenditure which is the Done Thing or unavoidable and another in the *reddest* ink for unpatriotic or *bestial* expenditure like cigarettes or juniper juice.

Well then the drill is at the *end* of the week I show the page to Haddock who will add up *both* columns which is a thing I *cannot* do, and *sign* the page, *after* which my dear for everything in the *red* column we buy an *equal* amount of these soporific *Saving* Certificates, *that* is of course if the cash is in sufficient supply, my dear it *is* rather a satisfying system don't you think and if you and Henry would like to try it by all means, only I don't suppose your Henry can add much can he, I *ought* to warn you perhaps that one small serpent is *just* perceptible, and that is *which* column to put *what* in sometimes, well today my dear what with the New Year burgeoning and the little bosom surging about and *warming* to the fellow-creatures I went to the Festering Gallery and bought rather a *bizarre* picture by Carl and Taffeta Brule for Haddock, you know darling or perhaps you don't poor rustic they're the couple who paint all their pictures *together*, I definitely can not envisage *why*, but there it is they're the most *electric* couple and *quite* penurious, so whenever I can I do the Christian thing, I can *not* pretend however that they magnetize my Haddock *much*, in fact he did once say that he'd swim the Channel on a *cold* night to avoid poor Taffeta, and it's true that the *last* picture of theirs I bought was one of those *rather* triangular women with *green* hair, which did take a *little* time to settle down in the home, though I *think* I do see what they mean now, it's the *pattern* and the composition and everything that *matters*, however *this* picture was *quite* unsimilar, my dear the *Pool* of London with the Tower and *Tower* Bridge and tugs and steamers and two barges with *enchanting* cinnamon sails, which I did think Haddock would like for his *study* because of old haunts and everything, well my dear I *purchased* impulsively and took him to see it, later, *without* however telling him it was a New Year *gift* for him, well my dear he gazed at it with *noticeable* aversion and *all* he said was Where is the *wind*, which of course I ought to have known because he is so tiresome about the wind in *pictures*, however, I said *Must* there be a wind perhaps it was a calm day, and he said *Look* at the *flags* the wind's easterly at one side of the picture and *westerly* the *other*, which I now perceived was *too* right, however I said I expect Carl painted one side and Taffeta the other only it was on different days, and anyhow I said don't you like the *sails*, at which he said *no* barge would have all those sails up above Tower Bridge and *this* one if the tide's flowing will charge into *London* Bridge and lose her *mast*, he also said the tug's funnel was *four* sizes too large, and *where* was the steamer's anchor-cable or something, so I said Oh well you don't want a *coloured photograph* and he said Yes he'd *much* prefer it, at which darling *gulping* down the tears I was *just* wondering if I could *cancel* the purchase when *who* should roll up but Taffeta and *Carl* all burbulous and grateful, *on* which of course the ghastly facts emerged, you should have *seen* Haddock's face, I must say he behaved *too* well, said *quite* nothing about the wind, and was *even* affable to Taffeta, however outside, and this is the *point* of the entire narrative, he said In *which* column will you put expenditure like *that*, so I said In the *Done Thing* Column of *course* because it *must* be the done thing to nourish the anaemic and subnutritioned artist even if he does *not* cause *unanimous* raving, so Haddock said Well you may be right my dove of course I *should* have said that *any* picture by Taffeta Brule should be in the *Bestial* Expenditure Column, on the *other* hand I do know *this*, that every time you buy a picture of a *triangular* woman with *green* hair *fifty* per cent by Taffeta Brule I am *not* going to put an *equivalent* sum in the *Savings* Racket, so there the matter rests darling, I *only* mention all this to show you the *kind* of enigma that *may* confront you if you and Henry take up the Topsy Loyalist Accounting System.

About my *other* Resolutions darling I doubt if I can reveal the *whole* soul now because on the *first* day of a *new* year as *you* know darling there *may* be the *faintest* indications of *fatigue*, however the *main* thing *as* I have said is the Torch and Beacon Movement, illuminating and beckoning to *all* the comrades and utterly determined *not* to enjoy oneself for *simply* years, of course Haddock says I've gone quite "masokist" or something, merely because I said *Why* do we women wear all these *garments*, why not *export* the lot to America and let us women go about in smocks and *sandals*, after all you can scarcely *see* a stockinged leg in London today so why not be *logical*, as a matter of fact I've made myself the *most* seductive though spiritual smock and came down to *breakfast* in it, but Haddock says I am *not* to wear it at the House or *anywhere*, which only shows you how difficult it is to be *helpful* economicly, oh dear, the best and briefest of years darling, your *frustrated* masokist TOPSY.

LETTER XIII

HEROIC ACT

January 9, 1946.

Trix darling, a *new* rule of life for you, *always* keep a little *holly* in the hall, I'll explain why in minute, *by* the way my dear *what* about the good *resolutions*, I *noted* sardonicly what you said about making Henry join the *Rotary* and circulate a little more, because I don't suppose a *thing* has happened and if I were you I'd abandon the *entire* aspiration, for one thing one has to attend on *all* the Fridays except about *one*, and Henry will only be *expelled* for non-attention like Haddock was, or do I mean *as* yes Haddock says I do, it's *too* clear from what you say that your Henry's reaching the *ungregarious* stage and when he's not *squelching* about his woods and spinneys prefers to be *quite* reticent and ruminative in the *home*, I know the signs, of course I don't mean that you mustn't do your best to *make* him utter from time to time, though *never* at the morning meal, and as for *people* my dear have a few *sprigs* and blossoms in from time to time and you'll see him expand like a *rose*, especially if they go slow with the *Scotch*, but Rotary or anything like that no *definitely* no darling, Haddock by the way is already smoking like a *volcano* again, only more regular, in *spite* of the dollar area, and as for my *accounts*, well they began *meticulously*, but *what* a pest and martyrdom they are, however about the *holly*, well I expect you've read about the wave of *delinquency* in our afflicted city, my dear *too* alarming, one day it's *jewels*, the next day it's cases of *tea* far more dejecting, and they took 57 turkeys from a local meatmonger, it's called *bulk*-purchase I believe, and of course *how* they flash about the city with all these *massive* ill-gotten cargoes, because my dear the *crowds*, one can scarcely *stir* with the merest *parcel*, and as for 57 *turkeys*, my dear *where* all the people come from and *where* they sleep is something I *definitely* can *not* envisage, well among them it seems are *exactly* ten thousand *deserters* who having no *ration-cards* are compelled to exist by grabbing diamonds, etcetera, I do *not* follow the reasoning utterly but there it is, my dear the other day the police *flooded* the West End and Haddock's identity things were scrutinized *four* times in half a mile, *too* thorough but as he said not *totally* convincing, because after all these deserters have to sleep *somewhere*, why not make the *most* loud and *alarming* pronouncements about *harbouring* deserters and let *no one* sleep a chap without examining a chap's *papers*, however I dare say there is a little more to it than *that*, and of course as Haddock says what with all the chaps having been in the Army where private property does not *exist* and all the chaps at home being told that private property is a kind of *crime* invented by the wicked Tories, it's not too surprising to find the *sense of property* a shade *sluggish* here and there, though of course in the same circles the bestial *profit-motive* does seem to struggle along somewhat, anyhow my dear in liberated London now we all look under *all* the beds, especially of course my *hunted* Iodine Dale, Oh I forgot, I *did* tell you didn't I that she's working out the last months of her *decree nisi* and is *quite* satisfied that the *King's* Proctor is after her because of the *hooded* man who lurks under the lamp-post the *rocket* blasted, doesn't it all sound *too* macaber and moving, personally my dear I think she's bats, but what can you expect and there after an absent week or two he definitely *is* again, or someone *like* him, I've *implored* Haddock to *visit* the King's Proc and find out for certain if he has any *hounds* about, but Haddock says *if* the great *wheels* of Justice are in *fact* in motion it wouldn't be the done thing for a *Member* to poke the old nose in *much*, if *any*, meanwhile the poor victim is in *such* a state of *nisi-neurosis* she makes me open *all* her letters in case it's the King's Proc or somebody and will *not* open the front-door if it's to take in the *bread*, though *too* helpful in the home elsewhere, in fact a godsend, because my angelic Mrs B is *quite* distracted with all her family demobbed and *how* to feed them, well my dear *last* night I said to Haddock, *Take* the pathetic waif to the pictures or somewhere before we all have an attack of *battery*, I'll guard the fort, so off they went, and my dear feeling *noticeably* Christian because there have been moments when I *rather* fancied he was *rather* attracted, I thought it's at least the *Fourteenth* Night let's get the Christmas vegetation down, so after a *heroic* act with the step-ladder up the basement stairs I did the schoolroom and the hall, *beginning* with that barbarous *holly*, which they say this year is more lacerating than ever, *too* right, *quite* agony, well then my dear when half-way up the ladder to dismantle the mistletoe there's the *rudest* knock on the *front* door *three* feet away, my dear the little heart missed *seven* complete beats and then fell into the larger intestine, the *brain* however was working like a *rocket*, I thought Well it *may* be the King's Proc, or it *may* be one of the new *inspectors* about erroneous war-works or *billetees*, but *intuition* tells me it's a *bandit*, because you know darling *sometimes* you absolutely *know* you're right, well I thought the done thing is to ring up that *magic number* for the *police* and *hold* the bandit till they arrive, only *could* I remember the magic number, *no*, yes I know now it's *999* but *all* I could think of was Terminus *1234*, so my dear I *slunk* into the schoolroom and dialled *that* which turns out to be the *Sunday Times*, well while I'm explaining to a *baffled* watchman or somebody there's another shattering knock at the door, and I think *Let's* face it *after* all it may be the Ministry of Health or *carols*, because my dear in these parts carols begin in November and go on till *March*, so I snatch up a bosomful of *excruciating* holly, *turn* the latch and scuttle back and up my *ladder* again, well my dear in at once comes the *most* scrofulous little man with his *hat* over his eyes and *shuts* the door, and he says *very* American, *This* is a hold-up, *stick* 'em up, well by this time believe it or not darling the little brain was working *exactly* like a *ball*-bearing and I said *That's* no way to talk to a British matron under the *mistletoe*, to which he answered Cut it out swell dame are you Mrs *Elkinstone*, so I said For that matter are you the Ministry of *Health*, and he said *Are* there any *guys* in the house, my dear believe me this is absolute *verbatim*, so I said *Several*, and I *then* perceived that the little vermin was trembling like an *aspic-leaf*, so I thought This is one of the *amateur* bandits, no more American than Stonehenge or *me*, so leaning gracefully over my ladder I caught him the *most* unfriendly *slosh* in the face with about *five* shillings' worth of holly, I then fell on top of him, *ladder* and all, my dear I'm *nothing* but scratches and bruises, but I was *on top* so I hollied him a *little* more till my dear he *mewed* for mercy, when leaving the body *entangled* in the ladder I darted to the phone and shouted *Bandits*, well of course I was still through to the *Sunday Times* man who was sweetly helpful and told me *all* about 999 which we arranged for *him* to ring but of course I'd hardly *begun* to give him my address and everything when we were cruelly *cut off*, and by then the *anaemic* bandit had crawled to his feet and *evaporated* into the night, *too* disappointing but *rather* a triumph don't you think, though of course Haddock and me are *scarcely* speaking because he doesn't think it was a bandit *at all* but some sort of *divorce* detective, who thought it was a *sage* way to get *evidence* of any illicit *man* on the premises, who of course would rush to repel *bandits* but not the Ministry of *Health*, but then I said Why *me*, well it seems there *was* a Mrs Elkinstone in these parts *years* ago, so probably it's some utter failure in the filing system, they've got the *wrong* address in the wrong Borough, and if so it means that my *haunted* Iodine has no more to fear from the *hooded man*, which is a *big* thing to the good, on the other hand Haddock says that for all we know I *may* have mangled one of the *King's Proctor's* men, which may be *high* treason or something, I must say I could hardly care *less*, farewell now your big bedridden bruise TOPSY.

LETTER XIV

TIMOTHY BRINE

January 16, 1946.

Trix, my distant woodpigeon, *sensation*, what *do* you think, I'm going to write a *book*, or part of it, or anyhow be *in* it, I know you never *glance* at my letters, but Henry does I *hope*, and perhaps he'll remember I told you about my *bandit*, the small-sized weasel I lashed and dispersed with cruel *holly* in the hall, well *what* was my astonishment yesterday he *telecommunicated* and asked if he could "contact up with me a coupla minutes", my dear as Haddock says it's *too* bizarre the *words* they waste these tough and snappy categories, because *contact* was pompous enough and *meet up with* was worse but when it comes to *contact up with*, when all you mean is *see*, however I said whatever *for*, and he said he reckoned he had to hand himself a *coupla* basinfuls of humble pie, by which my dear I *gathered* he meant *apologize*, so never yet having had an apology from a *bandit* I did the gracious, which Haddock to my surprise supported, so we made a date when Haddock could be there, Haddock by the way insisted on digging out the *rustiest* German weapon he brought back from the last war but *one*, for which praises be he has never had an *inch* of ammunition, because he said for *all* we knew there was dirty work in the offing still, he knew the type, which of course is *so* spurious, but my dear I must inform you that Haddock to my *mortal* shame reads

64

absolute *leagues* of all this toughery stuff, moaning the *entire* time What *muck* what *utter* muck but *wallowing* deeply and quite inconsolable unless there's a new Timothy *Brine*, who is perhaps one of the *least* intolerable, I did actually wade *womanfully* through one of his, but my dear *what* squalor, what *insanitary* English, nobody is *ever* shot except in the stomach, *everyone* talks like a hairy ape, there are *no* women only *dames* frails and floosies, and every third paragraph the detective has a *slug* of rye or *four* fingers of *Scotch*, my dear *where* they get all the whisky and *how* they do any *detecting* on it, in one book Haddock calculated in *one* night and day the G-man hero got rid of four bottles of Scotch and one of *rye*, and this was in the *Home* Counties *1944*, however *as* I say these works are manna to my respected Haddock, *what* is more it now appears he *rather* fancies himself as a psychowhatisit *student* of the underworld, anyhow he said he must sit with the gun in the *back* drawing-room in *case* my humble pieman was not on the *level* or the up and *up* or something, my *dear* what expressions, well at last my *adored* Mrs B who is doing a *brief* chore or two again now her breadwinner is better brings up the little bandit, who my dear *without* his hat looks littler than ever, *practically* invisible, and what with the *holly*-scars on his poor little face which is like the face of a backward *mouse* all the mother-bird is beginning to stir in me, when *judge* darling of my astonishment and dismay, before the bandit-waif has had time to open his tiny mouth I hear Haddock say *too* savagely *Stick* 'em up pal, and out of the shadow he comes with that laughable *pistol*, my dear *imagine* all this in a girl's *own* drawing-room, W6, well the little bandit puts his hands up and says *Look* dame, I kinda thought you and me was on the up and up, I thought maybe you'd let me get next to you *alone*, but now I guess I gotta take what's coming to me, well then Haddock said What's *beefing* you chum, or something, I'm gonna *frisk* you, maybe you pack a *rod*, at *which* my dear I merely *flopped* on to the sofa in a state of wonder and blush, too lowering, well Haddock went through all the little bandit's pockets, he found a tobacco-pouch, a *spectacle*-case, two pipes, a bit of *string*, a wallet, a box of matches, *quite* empty I need *hardly* say, and an envelope which he read out *too* suspiciously, To Timothy *Brine*, he said, Whadya know about Timothy *Brine*, well then my dear the little bandit said softly in the sweetest little Cockney voice, I *am* Timothy Brine, my dear I thought then that *Haddock* would fall in a faint, but it seems he told me afterwards it's the done thing with bandits never to show *surprise* at *anything*, anyhow all he said was, Look pal could you use a shotta *Scotch*, and the little man said Thank-you sir, with *lots* of water, and look here you needn't keep up the American I'm no more American than Westminster Abbey, even then darling it seemed Haddock could *not* throw off his part once started, because he said something like Listen boyo no funny business or I'll drill you so full of holes a *culinder*'ll look like it could hold a gallon of *rye*, which my dear will show you how *much* he's absorbed of this *unspeakable* imbecilery and *just* how deep the canker's gone.

Well, darling, while he's "fixing" the drinks as he now calls it I get the little ex-bandit to sit down and sorta draw him out, O gosh I'm *catching* it, my dear it's the *most* affecting story you *ever* heard, it seems he really *is* Timothy Brine, or rather he *isn't*, because his real name is *Cuthbert* something, he's a *library* assistant at *East* Wansey, and he has a widowed mother who's been dying for *years* and has to have *constant* operations and oranges and everything, well in off-hours at the library he read *all* the Tough Guy and Stomach-shooting School one after the other, till at last he said a little voice inside said *Cuthbert* boyo *you* can do this, *which* accordingly he *did*, though my dear he's never been *near* America, in fact the longest he's *ever* been absent from mother was a day-trip to Southend in *1939*, but you see he's *utterly* absorbed the atmo and the lingo from the *books*, which shows *how* pseudo it all must be, on the other hand he must have a little *swamp* of an imagination because my dear *some* of the episodes in the *early* works, however darling you know how they *sold* perhaps, and you must *always* remember that *all* this was in aid of a poor sick *mother*, but my dear *now* comes the thumping tread of tragedy and gloom, the poor sick mother *declines* to die, resuscitated of course by these *miasmic* but cash-creating books, what is more she now has *such* a high standard of dying so to speak, meanwhile my poor little chum thinks he's *drying up*, he's done the same thing over and over like they *all* do, yes my dear I *know* I mean *as*, and now he wants some more *reality* to mine and quarry, but of course he *can't* go to the States because of poor sick *mother*, and besides he'd probably be *slaughtered* by the Stomach-shooters *not* to mention the *authors* if they only knew, so the *pathetic* sweet has been picking the dust-bins for reality *here*, Haddock was *too* right the first thing he tried was *divorce* detective because nothing he thought poor innocent could lead a chap deeper into the cosmic midden, whereas nothing in *fact* it seems could be more respectable and *drab*, but he thought Well anyhow what a good *"front"* as they call it for burglary or banditry, moreover says he a chap who is practically *always* writing about hold-ups etcetera *ought* perhaps from time to time to do one *himself* if only to get the *psychowhatisit* accurate, which I think is *so* right don't you agree darling, *hence* anyhow as I've told you he makes his *trembling* assault upon the Haddock home, and of course *how* fruitful because I'm *too* sure that half the time the bandit's *bleak* with apprehension but no one *says* so, well then it seems he's *so* impressed with the Topsy technique and her *heroic* holly act, *about* which he's *quite* unresentful, he thinks I *must* get next to *that* dame, my dear *what* language, so the idea is, I gather, only of course there's *Haddock* who's *too* disappointed it's not a *real* bandit, *thrilled* up to a point to meet Timothy Brine, but slumped no little to find he's a Wansey *librarian*, and how far he'll be *quite* keen on my being the chief dame frail or *floosie* in a new Timothy Brine is an avenue still to be *explored* so to speak, however we've both promised to aid the little bandit *all* we can, if it's only some sage advice on dress or drink, and who knows we *may* reduce the stomach-shooting ration, and *even*, though too unlikely, get a word or two of *English* into the works, farewell your battling patriot TOPSY.

LETTER XV

THE DOGS

January 23, 1946.

Trix, you little *land-clam*, I'm *too* wounded about your reticent responses, I *empty* my bosom at you and *all* I get is an *unreadable* postcard, my dear for another halfpenny you can send an entire *letter* free of tax, but of course if you've taken to your *horse-hobbies* again I suppose you're *practically* always in a healthy *stupor*, by the way darling we were wondering the other night *has* anyone ever tried *eating* the fox, because after *all* that exertion, and surely the whole *conception* of the hunt is *food* for the hungry squaws and squawlers, of course I suppose it would disappoint the *dogs*, and Haddock says he thinks it might be *tough*, though *why* is an enigma because one gathers they eat *nothing* but the *most* expensive poultry, anyhow why don't you and Henry start a new breed of *eating*-foxes, *three* sizes larger, and make hunting a definite *drive* to supplement the *meat*-ration, in which case it might have a *permanent* niche in the *planned economy*, whereas otherwise it's *too* likely to be anti-social and the undone thing, if not denounced by *Uno*, the only *other* hope for you Haddock thinks is to somehow bring *betting* into it, because he says anything with betting in it is bound to flourish and *no* Government *dares* to so much as *sniff* against it, so perhaps you could have Four to one on the *Fox*, and *Ten* to one against Mr Peasepudding witnessing the *Kill* and so forth

and of course *mounted* bookmakers *galloping* among the
horsemen, changing the odds and *stimulating* the sternmost,
honestly my dear you must confess there *is* a sort of *marginal*
sanity to my at first sight *esotteric* and even *certifiable* suggestion,
well for example glance for a moment at these inconceivable
greyhound-contests, to which my, dear I used to *guiltily* creep
from time to time before the late conflict, and as a *matter* of fact
I've *just* begun to more or less *resume* the wicked ways, *not* of
course for self-*enjoyment* darling far from it, because my dear
following the dogs, which *by* the way is what you call *your*
quaint proceedings isn't it so you see we have got a *few* spots in
common, well *actually* it is about the *most* exhausting form of
human *toil*, my dear not a *moment's* peace, *incessant* arithmetic
which as you know was never my *ace* activity, and constant
bodyjostles with swarms of VUPs, which is short of *course* for
Very Unmagnetic Persons, no darling it's *purely* part of the *drive*
against the *overdraft*, because as Haddock *wistfully* reiterates
betting in this *bat-conducted* world is the *one* form of cash-
creation which is not taxed *at all*, and actually before the
conflict I did one year *create* enough to take the *entire* tribe of
Haddock to France, *too* satisfying, and this year if the twins are
back I *do* want them to have a *halcyon* holiday with *weeks* of
ozone, my dear I can *hear* you cackling but many a night as
Haddock will confirm when *yearning* for a *nice read* in a
soporific seat I've obeyed the better self and marched away to
martyrdom among the VUPs, who of course one *must* admit
may *all* have prolific families who are aching for the seaside *too*,
so perhaps it's not *quite* so anti-social as you *think*, though when
one sees the *figures* not to mention the VUPs, my dear do you
realize, Haddock says the dog-totes are taking nearly *twice* what
they did before the war, *seventy* millions a *year* I think he said
though of course a *mass* of that comes back in *winnings*, but my
dear *when* you think that in *three years* the money we put on
dogs and horses and *Arsenal* and what-not is more than the
entire American *Loan* one begins to perceive *just* what the

national hunger for the seaside must *be*, so to speak, and they say *why* there are *quite* no taxis in London is they're *all* waiting for wad-hunters at the *dogs*, I couldn't tell.

Well darling I don't want to ululate *too* soon, because it is *so* flattening when you think you have the *longest* holiday *practically* in the bank when suddenly those *irrational* beasts begin to do the *wrongest* things and day by day the little gainings dwindle, but *actually* at the moment we are about *ten* Peppiatts on the way to *Cornwall*, of course I'm behaving *quite* cautiously at present, sort of taking the *pulse* of things so to speak, but I rather think it's going to be *less* laborious to win a wad than it *was*, because you see in the old days one made an absolute *study* of the form and everything, *utterly* of course against my principles and *nature*, my dear I do feel in some things the little *intuition* is *practically* infallible, you can't *guess* how many times when I hear what's won the *Big* Race I say Yes I *thought* so I chose that horse this *morning*, by the *name*, in fact as Haddock says if *only* I'd backed them all we'd be rich enough to pay the *income-tax*, at one time that was my absolute *method*, because say what you like a good name is *half* the struggle, by the way darling *did* you see we're now talking about the *Soviet Ballet* which Haddock says is the utter *terminus* of twaddle, game set *and* match, because if there was one thing you *might* expect to go on being merely *Russian*, however he's got a bet with *two* Ambassadors that *before* Easter we shall hear about the Soviet *language*, and people will say they're learning *Soviet*, well to go back to my philanthropic dogs, by the way darling stiff and *stupefied* though you *may* be with indifference to *my* poor dogs you must recall what *weeks* of agony in time past I've suffered with a smile from hearing the news about *yours*, my dear shall I *ever* forget the day you found in Twillington *Bottom* and killed in Somebody's *Patch* after a *celestial* run, and Henry narrated me over *about* five counties, in and out of *covers* and ploughed fields, with hounds *feathering* and *faltering* and *footling*, is *that* right, my dear *too* defatigating, so darling put *one* more pillow behind the old back and *try* to concentrate on the primitive customs of the *capital*, I can see *no* plausible cause for your peering *snootily* at my little dogs, after all *all* dogs are *dogs* and it might be said that Henry and me were *twin* facets of British dog-love, not to mention the *chase*, because it's all very well for you to say that my dogs are hunting a merely spurious *hare*, half the time *your* dogs are after an imaginary *fox*, and anyhow *as* I was saying you bring *no* more back to the larder than *I* do, so, sorry darling I must look back to see where I *was*, Oh *yes* about the *form*, well when I began this *quite* serious dog-following phase I read *all* the dog-columns in *invisible* print, the little eyes became beady and dim, my dear I wouldn't *think* of backing a beast at *Wimbledon* unless I knew *exactly* what he'd done in the last *six* races at Harringay and *Howmuch*, *what* he beat, *which* trap, *how* fast, and what was the *weather*, my dear *protracted* and *lethal* labour, however *now* I gather, I expect you've read in the papers about the bizarre behaviour, my dear *sub-ethical* men spending the *night* in kennels and issuing suddenly with obtruse *drugs* so that every dog but *one* in a race resents running *about* halfway round, *too* ingenious, and now there are rumours of *more* uncivic devices, my dear in the old days one could stand *close* against the track and have a stirring view of the little yelpers, which is *actually* a decorative spectacle, *even* my dear when a girl's own dog is bitten at the corner and *then* beaten by a short nose, but now it seems they're going to push us *back* because they think *some* citizens may throw small rats, guinea-pigs, invisible *mice* or even *lizards* onto the course, *not* to mention drawing-pins and lumps of *glue*, so as to distract the doggies and frustrate the bookies, though *how* you can arrange for one dog to pursue a rat but not *another*, however personally I am positively in *favour* of all this, for one thing darling it brings the *whole* thing don't you think into line with *your* sport, the chances of the *chase* I mean, like the fox-dogs going off after a *sheep* or the fox being *headed* by an ugly governess, in fact if I were the management I should have *surprise* items in *every* race, *wild-cats* my dear and old bones and explosive *hurdles,* because think what a fearnought breed of *dog* you might develop, and then perhaps we could *export* it to America, *ranking* who knows with Scotch W. and the *race-horse,* but of course the *main* claim for the new technique is that it will cut out *nearly* all that petrifying nonsense about *form* and so forth, the whole thing will be a *genuine* gamble, I shall *merely* choose a *nice* name like I used to or sometimes possibly a nice-coloured *dog* and trust to intuition and natural *justice,* anyhow I must be off darling, I'll put ten bob on the *third* race for you, and tell Henry to think out about getting some betting into the *fox-field,* you must see what a *political* asset, I'm late farewell your industrious TOPSY.

LETTER XVI

JACK AND JILL

January 30, 1946.
Trix darling, *such* news what *do* you think *both* the twins may be out by *Christmas*, I've had the *longest* letters, by the way darling have you the *faintest* notion what a *Flag* lieutenant does, personally because they all call him *Flags* I thought our Jack would be in charge of *signalling*, well I know when they talk about *Pills* that's the *Doctor*, and *Guns* is the Gunnery King, and *Sparks* is the Wireless, so what would *you* think, although of course I ought to have known that *pure* logic like I *always* use is *quite* misleading and *redundant* in the Navy, because when they talk about *Number 1* they don't mean the *Captain* like I and you would, they mean Number 2 or perhaps not *that*, anyhow I forget if I told you Jack was *torn* off his beloved destroyer in the East and ordered to be this *Flags* in Australia, which from all I hear means a sort of *Mother* to an Admiral, who is it sounds the *most* lovable category, in Charm-and-merit group undeniably *One*, because Haddock met him at that *Mulberry* place, well Jack we gather has to nurse him through *parties*, the poor Admiral it seems being far from a *party*-type and creeps into corners *whenever* possible, *too* moving, Jack I suppose has to goad and *mobilize* him again into social combat, *what* wouldn't I give to see it, wouldn't *you*, anyhow he's having the *most* fruity *experience* and one gathers a congenial *time*,

74

though *rather* yearning of course to be back on his little *bridge*, but my dear the Australians have been *too* wide-hearted and wondrous to *all* the Navy *manifestly*, bless them, and if he doesn't come home with at least *one* Australian bride, which Haddock says he might *well* have done himself *but* of course for rather a *Topsy* priority, and of course *all* this is the *most* phenomenal coincidence because my dear I was *too* affected by what you said about your young and ours, and *numerous* salvos for the new *photos*, of *course* it would make me *mediaevally* happy to have a four-square wedding, *your* Fidelity and Jack, *your* Phil and Jill, my dear it sounds like a *nursery* rhyme, *too* touching, but how *could* you give that poor child a name like *Fidelity*, my dear *Punctuality* I could understand, *Tenacity*, *Veracity*, or even *Fertility*, but *Fidelity*, what a *bunker* to put on the green, my dear it's like labelling a hotel *Temperance*, when of course the *nicest* gentlemen will keep away *even* if they've no *desire* to drink, and of course *what* will happen when the poor child's *married* and her spouse perhaps is on the *China* Station, *nothing* in trousers will venture *near* her, because can you imagine any *nice* man *telecommunicating* to a grass-widow and saying *Fidelity* dear come *out* for a dine and dance, you might *just* as well have christened her *Nun* or *Goldfish*, and perhaps of course that was you and Henry's *plan*, however darling *don't* let us go into all that *now*, honestly I never meant to say a *word* about it, and of course I must tell you that Haddock is *absolutely* with us, I mean about the tribal *nuptials*, the only thing is I *do* think we don't want to *rush* things don't you agree my dear, because after all what *do* we know about the Young, honestly my dear in these days I find the Young are *so* inscrutable that I sometimes feel by the time we *understand* them they'll be practically middle-*aged*, and I do think there *may* be such a thing as incompatible *what* is the word, I *know* you'll understand darling, and then of course there's *environment* and everything, I mean just because you and I were *bosoms* at the old academy and *since* one mustn't be *too* sure about the next litter *must* we, pardon the metaphor my dear, as you know I'm rather *dog-minded* these days, by the way *last* Wednesday was a *pattern* of calamity, only *one* of my selecteds won and then it was a *foul* or something, *too* deflating *all* the little winnings went and I *do* so ache to finance the Haddock holiday, however as I was saying, well Jill for example, Jill and your Phil, my dear I can see at once he's the *grandest* boy, and *how* they've both filled out at Medicine *Hat*, or was it *Moose Jaw*, I suppose you *couldn't* have done anything about those front tusks darling, Jack had *much* the same formation at school but suffered *plates* for centuries, and *now* as you'll see, *too* sorry it's only a snap my dear and *not* in uniform, the *second* girl from the right we gather is a *rather* aromatic Wren Second *Officer*, no tooth-trouble *there* by the way, however what are *teeth* it's the *temperament*, isn't it, and *that* in passing is the word that baffled me *before*, well of course it *shines* out that your Phil is going to be a *country*-boy, which in theory I'm *utterly* for, my dear you know *whatever* I say I'm *never* so happy as *knee*-deep in mud or sneezing in the new-mown *hay*, Jill by the way my dear is a hay-feverite *too*, they say it's hereditary from Haddock's *great*-uncle who was the *first* Bishop of Sudonesia, which is some *leprous* segment of the *South* Pacific, of course I can *see* your large Philip *striding* through the spinneys with a gun like *Henry*, and it's *too* true that our little Jill has rustic trends *likewise* because for the first year and a *half* of the conflict she was *officially* a *Land* Woman, and they say she has the *most* magical touch with *cows*, for one thing in the *dank* and insanitary dawn she used to recite *pet* pieces from Haddock's *poems* to the cows, with it seems the *most* noticeable effect upon the *milk*, one time I *think* she said she got a prize for *octane* content, or is that *petrol*, it's all so *confusing* these days, anyhow that *is* our Jill, I mean with *any* animal she's like the Pied *Piper*, you can't walk down the *street* with her without a *platoon* of cats behind you, *too* embarrassing of course but *moving*, give her a moribund *sea-gull* or a half-drowned fish and she'll spend *days* with a brandy-bottle and *hot* wool *resusiuscitating* same, my dear what a *word*, and as for *dogs* they merely *swoon* at the sight of her and *lie* down in front of buses with all four *paws* aloft, actually my dear if you let her loose in one of your *fox-fields* I think it's too likely you'd find the fox and *all* the dogs in a voluptuous huddle on her *lap*, with all the horses queueing up for *sugar*, so at first sight you *might* say, I *couldn't* disagree with you *less*, that here you have two environmental *fits* or twin-souls, on the *other* hand one *has* to recognize, and I know my dear you won't for a *moment* suspect me of would-be *woundings*, the *one* thing the dear girl *never* does with her animals is to *shoot* them, and although of course *like* me she can wolf a roast bird *hot* or cold with *ill-concealed* relish, there it is I'm *too* afraid that if on the *first* day he takes her for a *spinney-stroll* with a gun and comes back with a bleeding *otter* or mutilated quail the tender child will give *three* screams and scurry back to *mother*, besides which she's *immersed* in music and could *not I* think live through a winter in the North without *hungering* for the Albert *Hall, don't* think I'm making difficulties darling, but it is just as well to face *realities*, as the burglar said to the bishop in the bath, of course you *may* say that Phil could get a job and settle in the *capital*, but *that's* a sacrifice if it was me I wouldn't *hear* of, my dear one thing a girl must *never* do and that is to stand between a hubby and a *hobby*, if you'll forgive that *pestilent* word, hubby I mean, no darling I'm *too* sure your Phil *must* stick to his beaver-shooting and everything, and the estate-agent job you mention sounds like *Nature's* niche for him, then of course there's the *age* conundrum, I don't know about your Fertility, but Jill will scarcely *notice* a man under *about* 43, I suppose it *is* true that the boys are backward especially the Brigadiers and *Wing*-Captains, bless them, anyhow *don't* let's worry or rush for an *instant*, the *moment* they're all present we'll have a *mass*-rally, give the little things their heads, and *philosophically* behold the outcome, but it *would* be magical I *do* agree, farewell Mrs England, the *nation's* matron TOPSY.

LETTER XVII

KEEPING FIT

February 6, 1946.

My dear Trix, I *do* wish I had a *single* clue to your *maze* of a mind, honestly my dear how *could* you be umbrageous about my *dove-like* letter, you know I meant *quite* nothing about poor Phil's teeth, *actually* I can't recall a word I *said*, only *as* a mother one does tend to *notice* little details *doesn't* one, but of *course* he's "good enough for Jill" you little clucking-duck, the only *phantom* of a doubt was about the adjustability of *environments*, I mean a boy might have teeth like a champion *crooner* but if his *main* delight was eliminating *badgers* he wouldn't *necessarily* be the best bet for *my* sensitive offspring, and even there I'm *far* from dogmatizing, because who knows, my dear at one time I couldn't handle a naked *plaice*, but two Yules back, with the aid of fire-water and a gas-mask, I disembowelled an entire *goose*, so it only shows, anyhow, *all* I meant was to *mildly* deprecate undue *precipitation*, my dear in these days *never* cross your bridges till you're *quite* the other side, and of course *personally* I wouldn't *presume* to give advice to *either* of my young, so what *is* the benefit of you and me beginning an unnatural bicker in the *dark*, you *do* understand darling, and perhaps if you think over your *mortifying* letter you'll put on the snowshoes, *slide* down the village, and send me the *softest* little *golden* telegram of grovel and *regret*, however not a word more about that *now*.

78

My dear it's *too* shaming, after a *mere* month the Topsy accounting system has *quite* disintegrated, for one thing the entries in the *red* column became *so* numerous that Haddock mutinied about buying *Savings* gadgets to *match*, I *dare* say by now darling you've utterly forgotten what the system *was* and if so it's *too* immaterial, because suddenly in the bath I had a luminous *moment*, I said *What* after all are these squalid accounts *for*, for nothing but to show if you're spending *too* much, and *what* is the purpose of having a *Bank* and an overdraft and all those *enervating* documents about *Self* they send you, except to give the same grim information, *officially*, my dear as Haddock said *why* keep a siren and yell the little *lungs* out, anyhow my dear large ledger is now in service with Haddock for *press-cuttings*, so closes another epoch in the upward struggle, but *don't* think for an instant there's any *general* weakening, *quite* otherwise, not *one* cigarette has sullied the lips this *year*, in fact I'm now *practically* in the *offensive* stage when one looks *scorpions* at the loose-livers who merely *offer* you a smoke, yesterday my dear I *positively* heard myself saying *Oh* no I *never* do, with the little nose trending skyward *noticeably*, about the juniper-juice the record is not *exactly* parallel, but considering the *ice* and *snow* and everything, and my dear at these *public* dinners one simply *has* to have an anaesthetic of *some* sort, in fact I find *wherever* one has *much* discourse with strangers of the human tribe, do you find that darling, do you *never* feel you'd like to withdraw to a nunnery with a nice *book*, and nowadays I've met *so* many people I simply *cannot* recall who any of them *are*, *too* embarrassing, whereas after a *reasonable* juniper-juice or two one either remembers or it couldn't matter *less*, by the way it's *too* heroic to hear that Henry's joined the *Rotary* after all, but *don't* be surprised if he comes back and drinks *heavily*, because I'm *not* persuaded that he can stand his fellow-men in the mass for *long*, unless perhaps it was in woods and spinneys, and even then, where was I, Oh yes, well in *spite* of the set-back mentioned there's still a spectacular drive for the *care of the body*, which is the main thing *after* all, my dear the scales have *scarcely* fallen from the little eyes when I'm *rolling* the *abdominal wall*, in *bed*, that's the beauty of it, of course darling I don't suppose you've ever given a *moment's* reflection to the abdominal wall, which is *so* shallow of you, because it *is* the absolute *foundation* of human goodery, my dear you know those muscles down the *sides* of the tummy, I dare say after all your horse-work you've got *steel girders* there but of course we poor townswomen, well it seems it's like a *paper-bag*, if you *don't* keep those muscles tough *quite* all the inside *gravitates* to the bottom of the bag, and *hence* the middle-aged *spread*, well there are two *mellifluous* exercises Haddock got from a man called *Hornibrook*, who says it seems we were never *designed* to go about *upright*, which accounts for everything, and one must admit you never see a *horse* with a middle-aged spread, or *do* you, I shouldn't know, whereas the only *humans* who escape are the *savages*, because they do *ventrifugal* dances, *thus* toughening the abdominal *wall*, well they're *too* easy and require *no* standing about in draughts and *undies*, you can roll the old wall in the *bed* in the bath or *anywhere*, in fact Haddock says he *has* rolled his in the House and on the Underground, and he says a *delicate* roller could make a speech from the Front Bench rolling the wall the *entire* time and nobody would *know*, though whether it would be the done thing, anyhow the little abdo is as flat as a *floor* and even Haddock's is *practically* invisible, besides which I must say the whole interior economy could *not* be more efficient if it was *nationalized*, so darling if you have the flimsiest doubts about your abdo I'll show you the *whole* drill when you come up, but then of course comes the macaber moment when one has to leave the hot-bottle and do the *normal* exercises in a Siberian *draught*, to which I still stick spasmodicly, though according to the Hornibrook School their merit is meagre compared with abdo-rolling, I mean the toe-touchers and *trunk*-twisters, and complex deeds with *chairs* and towel-horses, my dear there's one *captivating* exercise where you put *both* feet in the handkerchief drawer and stand on your *hands* with the *eyes* shut and everything *utterly* relaxed, I forget who told me about it but it's supposed to *liquidate* the entire frame besides mentally at the same time putting the *cosmos* in the true perspective first thing in the morning, and I must say *after* it I feel I can face the Queue Age with a *whistle* in the heart though *too* terrified that the hanky-drawer will descend on me *again*, which it did on *Boxing* Day when demonstrating to Iodine Dale, then of course there's the *mental* gymnastics, because I do agree it's *too* fallacious to care and cosset the *body* merely, I mean it may be malnutrition or the Arctic air-conditions, but I *sometimes* feel the little *mind* is *wizening, you* know like a neglected *walnut*, or perhaps the little *soul* is at last asserting itself, because my dear I'm *too* contented having esoteric *brooding*, but *can* I remember anybody's *name*, and *can* I concentrate on a funny story or an article on Bretton *Woods*, my dear *yards* before the point approaches I can feel the eyes glazing and the *soul* is reaching for the stars *elsewhere*, which of course is *quite* anti-social, so we've started a *joint* mind-and-body Movement, with special drills for *memory* and *concentration*, well for instance *every* day we learn a *piece* by heart, it may be Byron or Beachcomber or a *few* lines from the *Telephone* Directory, and the done thing is to say it off before *bed*, then whenever Haddock hears a laughworthy story he has to swear to *exactly* repeat it, and when I catch him at a leading article I say *Briefly* explain what it was all *about*, which *too* often has the poor man *yammering*, as for me I learn special verselets of an *exalting* category to recite during my *exercises*, thus you see bringing mind and body into *utter* harmony and dedisintegration, so altogether you see we're not *letting* go, all the same I've still got the *most* barbarous *vibrositis* in the back of the neck besides *occasional* pangs of intercostal or ribby *neuritis*, which Haddock attributes *entirely* to the *exercises*, Oh dear I must go and take my Vitamin B10, farewell you *have* abandoned your umbrage *haven't* you, *several* salvos your tenacious TOPSY.

LETTER XVIII

THE CANAANITES

February 13, 1946.

Trix darling for sheer miscellaneous *frustrating* mess the last week has been the *conqueror*, for one thing more *Iodine* trouble, but I think about that a little *reticence* perhaps, you *do* understand don't you, because my dear between you and I it seems the King's Proctor is *actually*, my dear the hunted child sees detectives *everywhere* and yesterday she screamed like a pig at the cannery when she opened the door to my melting *milkman*, and I forget if I told you about the policeman and Mrs B, as a result of which, however *no* more now dear I promised *positively*, another *major* trauma is that Haddock's secretary has got *maniacal* influenza or something, so once more I'm *floundering* in the *swamps* and fogs of his *correspondence* like I did *quite* all the war, while you were stowing the calories away at Medicine *Hat*, or was it *Moose Jaw*, my dear you've no *conception* the *letters* these poor publics get, heart-aching life-tales to which there's *no* answer, divorce-narratives by the dozen and the *mile*, *page* after page, with *quires* of enclosures, sometimes my dear it takes an *age* to hound down the *point*, and then you find the poor pathetic has been to *three* solicitors and turned down by the Courts, so *no* answer again except *Too* sorry, *quantities* by the way about the old decree nisi, to *which* we answer *No* more Private Members' Time *ask* HM *Gov* love, then of course *prolific* moans about demobbery and *students* and *housing* inequities and India and the GI *widows* and Palestine, my dear why don't you *make* the Gov do this that and *everything*, well if the letter's *legible* and not *too* corrosive or crazy you send it on to a *Minister*, and *how* I pity them, then you tell the *chap* what you've done and *bang* goes twopence-half-penny, the Minister *ultimately* sends you the *sweetest* answer which you forward to the *chap*, *another* two-and-a-half d., and *till* recently of course *another* for the letter to the *Ministry*, which is now *privilegious* and free thanks be, though it's true the stamp-bill is still *stupendous*, and of course *if* the chap gets an *effective* answer he generally writes to *thank* us etcetera and asks us to be dynamic about some *new* conundrum, so my dear it *quite* never ceases, and sometimes I do a *little* ache for the good old *bombdays* when we did actually lose a complete *slag-heap* of unanswerable letters by fire and water and the King's *enemies*, bless them, and as far as I know *no one* was *noticeably* the worse, well then besides of course *all* the loons and fearnought *pioneers* seem to write to Haddock, in *procession*, the other day there was the *most* protracted letter from an Indian asking Haddock to propose *polygamy* in the House, and my dear *too* plausible and public-minded, because of the *two* million redundant women and the relundant *birth-rate* and everything, and he said if the B Parliament does the high and haughty about polygamy well what about the B *Empire* which merely *swarms* with polygammers, *too* awkward to answer I thought, so I sent it on to John Simon's *Population* Commission, and I *do* see, well for one thing it *would* mean a little *help* in the home, which otherwise on all the evidence will *quite* never happen *again*, only I've told Haddock that if he *does* have two she must never *enter* my kitchen except *after* meals, when I shall be drier and she'll do the *sinking, she* shall answer *all* the letters and hardly *ever* speak, and I will *not* have a neurotical type like Iodine *Dale*, that's all, well then there was the indignant old boy of *73* who was *too* inflamed because he couldn't marry his *step-niece*, 59, which as far as Haddock and me knew he *could*, why *not*, but that will show you, *not* content with wanting you to alter the *laws* they expect you to alter the Forty-nine *Articles* then of course my delicious Canaanite, who my dear has a *complete* solution for the Palestine enigma, game set *and* match, because he says all this chat about the Israelites and the *Arabs* is *too* misleading and *unhistorical*, because what about the Canaanites who were there centuries before *anyone* and were the peaceful victims of unprovoked *aggression*, which one must admit if you forget about the Promised Land is *one* way of looking at it, of course the Philistines have always had a bad press but even they were there *first* though aggressors *likewise* one gathers, my dear it's all *too* complex what with Phoenicians and *Hittites* and Aryans from *Crete*, and the old boy sends us *immense* geological *trees*, because he says he's a *pure* Canaanite and lived at Joppa till the Zion-troubles when he left in umbrage with his *Committee*, who it seems are *all* Canaanites, including one Phoenician and two *Hittites* I *think* he said, my dear I believe they're *all* at the *Savoy*, anyhow their signature-tune is *Canaan* for the *Canaanites*, because he says once the *principle* is accepted the *other* controversy would be out-of-date and morally short-*circuited*, though no doubt he says the Canaanites would graciously agree to *partition* the land between the Jews and *Arabs* which some say is the only way, so that *theoreticly* perhaps, anyhow he wants Haddock to take him to see *Bevin*, and then for Bevin to go into the *entire* Canaan "incident" at *Uno*, my dear *who* was the *aggressor* and everything, under one of these unreadable *Charters*, well you *may* sit up there darling in your rustic sanctuary and say Of course the man is *bats* or *bottles*, which I must admit was my own *immediate* repercussion, because Haddock seems to be the main *target* of the bat-population, one poor woman writes weekly to say that 9^1/2 *years* ago he made a *solemn* vow with the Editor of *The Times* to care and foster her, another says she's Queen *Elizabeth* and the people ought to be *told*, but Haddock says that a public fellow *can't* be too careful, because he says how *few* the New Movements which *didn't* seem to be utterly bat-like when they *began*, and it *may* be his *duty* and everything, however I must say he's been *too* uneager about his duty *so* far, *quite* declining to answer the letters or even *look* at the geological *trees*, I have to write *boracic* postcards to say that Haddock's in *Denmark* and flying's prohibitive, *now* he wants me to explore the avenues and ask the Canaanites to a cocktail somewhere, which seems to me to be *too* unsuitable, the name by the way is *Moussa* which reminds me of something I can *not* think *what*, I've searched through Exodus and most of *Judges* but Moses is the one name near it and he you see was the other *side*, of course *one* hypothesis is that it's a *new* move in the *crime*-wave, like nearly *all* things, my dear these days one doesn't *think* of smiling at a stranger, and as for giving a *lift*, for fear of being *held up* or *pulped down*, or of course it *might* be one of the *King's Proctor's* men, a *diabolical* move against poor *Iodine*, Gosh I've had an *idea*, stand *by*!

Darling I've *just* telecommunicated to my little friend *Jean* who practically *runs* the Savoy, I *think* you met her at that fraternal *chemist's* the day Henry had his *classic* hangover and we gave him pharmacuticle *pick-me-ups*, anyhow she says there *is* a man called Moussa in the hotel, but no sign of a *Committee*, and no *Hivites* or *Philistines* as far as she *knows*, but she says he does look *exactly* like a Canaanite, as a *matter* of fact it seems he got his room by *mistake* because they thought he *must* be one of their *Unos*, *too* secretive it seems, has *all* his meals upstairs, and stalks out at *nightfall*, Oh yes and they *rather* think he's got an *animal* in a *basket*, which of course bangs an absolute drum with *me* because I now remember *Moussa* was the name of the *snake-charmer* we saw at Luxor, it's *too* true that Haddock says *our* Moussa is *dead*, but it's all *beginning* to check up a *little* don't you think, though whether the *snake* is intended for Iodine or *Uno*, however more later your distracted TOPSY.

LETTER XIX

STIFF LIPS

February 20, 1946.

Trix darling it's *too* likely that *this* despatch will read like the ravings of a sick *bat* or the *dribbling* of wolves in the Soviet forests, because the fact is I've got the *most* insanitary and stupefying *cold*, which of course is *so* deflating, because last autumn for *weeks* I had those fallacious *injections*, now I've taken *Nazrine* and *Noblo* and *Eumucia* and *Antitarrh*, which Haddock says is the *most* odious violation of language *yet*, in spite of which I'm still a mere perambulating sneeze, *all* my hankies and most of Haddock's are a *swamp*, and the washing these days comes back *half-yearly*, and of course if only all those *obscene* professors would stop mutilating the atom and do a *drive* against the cosmic *cold*, by the way darling you know what a *trend* I have for being right and you *may* remember what I told you *seasons* ago about their doing radar to the *Moon* and the British *Plan* for an expedition and everything, because you were *too* incredulous and septical at the time, but now the first part has been released *official*, about the radar I mean, so who knows about the *rest*, not *yet* of course because the first result would be a scene in the *Security* Circus and as a matter of fact though don't *whisper* about this they *rather* think *Kamschatka* may have got wind already and raise the whole question of planetary spheres of influence *quite* soon, anyhow darling do try not to sniff *too* loudly at our humble efforts to enlighten and *prepare* you, which reminds me *years* ago deny it or not the *moment* you were redeployed from Medicine Hat I told you that *almost* everything looked like being far worse than *ever* in the war, *too* right, my dear even the *Cabinet* have noticed it now, of course I think you're *so* sage not to *glance* at the papers, because these days honestly one sees a death sentence in every *column*, every day some childlike Minister discovers there's *no* coal, *no* fat, *no* wheat, *no* rice, and *no* houses likely for *several* years, that's the latest, and *quite* soon it seems it may be *no* films and no *fags*, well of course *as* I've said we never expected it to be *much* different, in fact Haddock wrote *before* the Election *God* help the men who rule the coming years, *whichever* party, as you know I *always* think the Christian thing, and one *can't* be unsorry for the wistful Ministers crashing and splashing in the cosmic bog, the only thing is that if there'd been *rather* less cockahoopery about *planning* and everything and a *little* less carbolic yap against the other fellow, the other fellow my dear being half the population, well perhaps the burning tears of compassion *might* flow more cataracticly *still*, as it is they're *mainly* devoted to the afflicted British wife and *matron* whose belt by now is so full of holes it's practically *porous*, and of course the *cardinal* thing is how it all mounts *up*, my dear in the old days with this *mephitic* cold one would merely have crawled into the bottom of a bed and lain there *moribund* with *two* bottles till consciousness returned, whereas now one has to be up and coping if one has the *bubonic* because my dear queues and coupons wait for NO girl and what with stiff-upper-lipping in a bronchitical queue, and searching the snow for *nutrimentary* fragments the cats may bring in from propinquous dust-bins, yes darling that may be the *faintest* atom of exaggeration but *not* more, and if anyone says *Dunkirk* to me again I shall *scream, four* times, though of course I do agree that the only *authentic* targets for censure and corrosive talk are the *septic* Germans and the leprous *Japs*, in fact if all else fails and the little upper lip relaxes somewhat I merely mutter *over* and over again, "GDG" and "GDJ" which my dear I will *not* interpret in case your Fertility, *too* sorry, Fidelity sees it, but the *last* letters stand for "the Germans" and "the Japs," *do* try it darling if you suffer *ever*, you'll find after about *seven* times you see the cosmic mess in *absolute* proportion with *warm* feelings for HM Gov, *always* excepting of course that *phenomenal* blot, my dear you know how I *hate* to say an unkind thing and even now I will *not* use *names*, but my dear *if* you guess I do think you'll agree that his charm-group is *not* high, in fact there is *something* to be said for the Haddock theory that he *is* congenitally *unmagnetic*, but that I know is *not* warm-hearted forget *quite* everything I've said.

Haddock my dear I hardly *see* these days, not that with this blinding cold I should always *recognize* him, partly because he's *too* busy preparing for the *Siege of London* when he says there may be no *Anything*, one hypothesis he harbours is that there may be *edible weeds* in the bed of the Thames, which of course has its plausible aspect, when you *think* of all the organic whatisit, I mean all the vegetational stuff from up the river, the *dead* cats the live gulls and all those millions of revolting little *pink* worms we use for newt-nutrition in the *summer*, anyhow at low tide he digs *doggedly* in the darkest mud, and boils his weeds for *twenty-four hours* though on *what* principle, anyhow the house is *permanently* dank with the *most* discouraging *alluvial* smells, after which we have a *tasting* to see if edible, *if* not which praises be has always been the verdict *so* far, the *next* investigation is *is* the weed *smokable*, which my dear means *protracted* dryings *all* over the kitchen and my *own* oven *too* inaccessible because of *steaming* water-growths smelling like I can *not* envisage what, my dear *too* redolent, *not* content with which he does *poisonous* experiments in the old pipe with *ground* bulbs and *dried* carnation leaves, my dear my beloved winter-plants are *quite* naked not to mention the cat who eats them *shamelessly*, then of course there are the *roast* bayleaves from the neighbour's tree and blotting-paper *boiled* in vinegar and dried *slowly* over gas, which Haddock says is perhaps the best, though as I *did* murmur *how* he expects to find enough blotting-paper and vinegar to supply the *nation*, not to mention *gas*, but there it is he says the days are coming when there'll be *quite* no *tobacco* to smoke and *how* degrading if a nation of fumigators is caught without *alternative*, which of course I do *so* see, because HM Gov you can bet a billion will open wide their virginal eyes and be taken by *astonishment*, all the same I do wish *some* of the experiments could be done in a Government *windtunnel* or somewhere *quite* elsewhere, the *one* ray of hope and solace is that after all these experiments Haddock seems to be developing almost an aversion to the smoking act, I mean after the *bayleaves* I could *not* induce him to use the *gift-cigar* from my delicious Dane the captain of the *Rota*, who has been over again with *tons* of butter and miscellaneous pig-fruit though not it seems for you and me but the Combined *Food* Board, which means I suppose some unworthy *foreigner*, what a *redundant* nuisance that Continent *is* well don't you agree darling, when you think of the *centuries* they've caused us trouble, and if *only* Adam had been an Englishman what *worlds* of worry would have been *quite* eliminated, by the way I've heard not a *word* more about the Canaanite, and so far the King's Proc has made no *positive* move against my *persecuted* Iodine Dale, who still has spasms when the *postman* knocks, altogether darling the turmoil of Peace is by no means abated, I was going to say well anyhow there are no sireens or doodle-bugs only whenever I do say that I dream about them *at* once so I won't, and of course the *sterling* solace is to think *how* often before the *best* people have seen the *end* of everything *just* round the corner, whereas peeping round it I seem to see an endless vista of the largest *hams* with mountains of enchanting *butter*, on which heroic note farewell your tight-lipped little TOPSY.

LETTER XX

MOVEMENTS

February 27, 1946.

Trix darling that *garrulous* Uno has departed *at* last and now perhaps we may have a little *peace*, my dear not a *moment* too soon one gathers because Haddock says the *next* thing was to be *Patagonia* presenting a letter from *Brazil* protesting about there being Russian troops in *Bornholm* which belongs to my delicious *Danes*, by the way darling I don't suppose you could care *much* less but why all this *incessant* twitter about *Indonesia*, in the old days there used to be an island called *Java* because we nearly went there from Ceylon and didn't they grow *jellies* there or was it *chutney*, and *Java* it seems is what they nearly always mean by *Indonesia*, anyhow that's the place where *Surabaya* is because I've just *hunted* it down in my bijou Atlas, but why *Indonesia* always, because I've looked *that* up in the Encyclopaedia which my dear is *so* flattening because it's *quite* always the *wrong* volume and nothing of the flimsiest interest is ever *mentioned*, however *estimate* my astonishment it says that Indonesia means *eight* different areas, from *Madagascar* to Borneo and the *Philippines*, so you *might* think from the papers that our *ubiquitous* troops were fighting in Madagascar which is *French* or bombarding the Philippines which is *Yankland's, too* ambiguous, well then I looked up little *Java* where it says the people are the *Javanese* "proper" the Sudanese and the

91

Madurese, my dear not one *word* about *Indonesians*, Oh and it says that Java was first mentioned in the *thirteenth* century, which *if* so *why* must we have the longest new name for it *now*, honestly my dear as if there wasn't enough *natural* chaos in the news, to mislead and mystify with *synthetic* hares of that sort should definitely be the undone thing, and *Indonesia* Haddock says means *Indian Islands* which of course makes the entire fuddlery *too* clear you *must* agree, Haddock by the way has internal umbrage because he's *always* said he's the *one* man of letters who's swum from Waterloo Bridge to *Westminster*, but now he's discovered that *Byron* swam from *Lambeth* Bridge to *Blackfriars*, so he's merely counting the days till he can swim from Vauxhall to *Southwark*, my dear these *men*, I only hope he doesn't start laughing and *sink* like he did last time and *all but* drowned off Cleopatra's Needle, have you noticed that my dear, no I remember you were never a *convincing* nymph in the water, but personally if I laugh in it I go to the bottom like a shiny little *stone*, meanwhile we're an absolute hive of *Movements*, not content with Liberate Bornholm, about which we're giving a *Foodless* Dinner with *No* Speeches, my dear I think it's *such* a sanitary notion don't you, because honestly how *few* the Movements which have *not* been practically *wrecked* by a Lunch or Dinner in aid of, one's pinned down between some *unelectric* stranger in charm-group *53* and some poor sweet who's doomed for a speech, *mutters* vacantly whatever you say and can't pass the *mustard* without intimidation, the feeding takes so long there's no time for even *one* sufferable speech, there are always *exactly* three times too many with *as* a rule at least two *shockers*, and *no* hope of slipping out for a *wash*, meanwhile in these days one drinks toast after toast with *nothing* in the glass which I think is *so* barbarous and Haddock says is *too* likely to set up a *lasting* frustration-canker in the *sub*-conscious, well as the hours pass one develops a slow but *smouldering* antagony to the Cause *whatever* it is, my dear I remember years ago going to an *Anti-Noise* dinner which Haddock was entangled in, and at the end of it I merely *ached* for noise, I was *starving* for noise, my dear I went out into the street with Haddock and *shouted*, he thought I was *dehinged*, I sang in the Tube and *safe* home I turned on the wireless put on a record and played the *piano* until my dear *forcibly* restrained by Haddock, so that will give you a *kind* of clue to what I mean, well my dear you remember the *prelimary* stages of a public meal, when everybody's *just* arrived *too* bright and bonhomous, the frock fits, the face-work is *intact*, a little juniper-juice is available, one meets an ancient bosom or *apprehends* a new, *if* one is introduced to the unelectric or submagnetic type one can slide away *shortly*, and for a *brief* space one is *practically* content to be among one's fellow-creatures, but *then* comes the *lowering* moment when they say *Dinner* is served, at *that* moment one finds one has *no* hanky, Haddock comes back from the eating-map and says he's sitting *about* a quarter-of-a-mile away, and I am between the *only* two *incurably* septic men he *knows*, the starboard shoulder-strap carries away, and one rather wants to be *slightly* sick, well darling the plan is that at *that* moment we *don't* go into dinner after *all*, in fact it's not settled utterly but I *rather* think we shall have it announced, Dinner will *not* be served, because I do so love to give happiness and *see* it happen, and I can *just* envisage the *wave* of radiance going over the faces when they realize they've *not* got to sit through a festering dinner or suffer a *single* debilitating speech, they can trickle away to the club when ready or have a *cosy* sardine over the fire in the home, *meanwhile* of course the juniper-juice will circulate briskly and one will wander about and whisper *Bornholm*, I can't *think* of a better technique for keeping a Cause warm and fragrant in the mind can you, of course you *may* say it's only a cocktail-party *disguised* but personally I see the most *esotteric* difference, for one thing it has the element of *surprise*, and then of course one will wear one's pretties and you'll have the *dignity* of the one and the brevity of the *other*, then of course I'm *too* concerned about Haddock's *Beacon* Movement, my dear you remember or don't you the Belisha Beacons, which however mocked were a *meritorious* notion and the one thing that gives a pedestrian any *hope* of a future, because as long as he gives reasonable notice it's *not* the done thing to mow him down between the studs, in fact the motors are supposed to *slow* and let him over, nor darling does it *matter* one hoot, as you'd better tell your Henry in *case* he brings the car which I do *not* advise the streets being *quite* impassable and insanitary with car-purloiners, where was I, Oh yes it does *not* signify if the orange blob is absent through blitzing because they made a *special* law in the war, but my dear as Haddock says does a *single* driver know all this, or if he does could he *conceivably* care *less*, *too* often he says when making stately passage through the studs he's merely *blown* off by the rudest hoots and has to leap a cubitt or two to escape some *rocketing* vehicle, on one occasion *quite* splitting the gastrocnemious *muscle* and he was a cripple for *weeks*, and of course the town is full of the *most* alarming *demobbed* drivers who still feel they're in charge of *tanks* or *ten-ton* lorries, and as for pedestrians they might just as well be *Belgians*, my dear Haddock was in one bus which *quite* evidently the driver thought was getting ammunition up to *Arnhem* under *fire*, roaring round the corners on *two* wheels, up-rooting lamp-posts and scaring *half* Chelsea into their *basements*, well Haddock says the police can do *nothing* being *far* too few and the one thing is for the citizen to *act* and *educate*, because apart from the drivers he says there is not *one* doe-pedestrian who *dares* to exercise her rights, they merely *huddle* on the pavement in the usual way until there are *no* cars visible when they scuttle across like frightened serfs, so my dear he meanders round the town solemnly crossing *all* the Belishas he can find, *noting* the behaviour and making *indignant* gestures if the vehicles swoop on impervious as they *nearly* always do, my dear one day I *know* he'll lose a hindleg or *worse*, well then he *yells* after the ruffian like a mad thing, and *if* he stops which they *sometimes* do they have the *most* carbolic altercation, *too* fruitless because most of them have not the *faintest* what H is talking about and *if* they do they say it's *nonsense* because of course the mere *conception* of *any* vehicle slowing down for a mere *foot-serf* is *against nature* to most of them, however that's the *Movement*, Haddock says if he *does* die on the King's High Way which is a safish bet at least he'll have perished for the *people*, and now he's made a new Will to say he's to be *cremated* and the ashes scattered over the driver who kills him excuse the macaber note darling, no more now TOPSY.

LETTER XXI

ULCEROUS WORLD

March 6, 1946.

Trix darling what an *ulcerous* world this is, don't you agree, what with *Quit* This and Quit *That* the poor old Briton seems to be cosmicly *redundant,* and the next thing *too* likely it will be Quit the *Planet,* for which *personally* speaking I'm almost ready at *once,* because my dear the festering inflated men who seem to breed in almost *every* latitude, of course the *loudest* laugh for *several* centuries was when we read about "the *wave* of national aspiration" in *Cairo,* which my dear would have been a *fraction* more impressive perhaps in 1942 when Mr Rommel was practically at *Shepheard's,* you know my dear how I *hate* to say an unkind thing and of course it's *too* possible that *bags* of evidence may have gone *astray,* but I can *not* recall any *epic* narratives about the Egyptian urge to battle against the septic *Germans,* now however I see that *all* the students are declaring war against the brutal *Briton,* by the way darling a thing I'm always *aching* to know, can you tell me *what* part of the day the foreign student spends in *study* because from all accounts he puts in *so* many man-hours at demonstrations, *barriers,* stone-throwing and *ultimatums* he can't have *too* much leisure for *lectures,* I now see that 2,000 *Chinese* students have been vociferating Quit *China* to the Russians, Haddock my dear says the *laughable* thing though perhaps not practical would be if suddenly we *did* quit everything, not utterly he says but just put all the soldiers in the ships, stand off about *six* miles, sardonically observe what happens and wait for the SOSs, meanwhile he's got a new Quit Britain movement for the *EAW*, which means I *know* you've guessed the England's Always Wrong boys, because honestly *why* they don't go to Jugoslavia or somewhere, my dear have you *seen* the sort of thing they say about that poor sweet General *Anders* who has been wounded at least *five* times altogether fighting the septic Germans, my dear in 1939 he fought for 28 days incessantly until can you believe it he finds he's being attacked by the Germans on one side and the *Red* Army on the *other*, he's then captured by the Russians and kept in jail for *quite* two years, until of course the suffering Russians are *driven* into the war, he's then *graciously* permitted to fight the Germans *again* and he and his lads do hero-stuff from Cassino to Bologna, now if you please the Polish Government says that his troops are not entitled to wear their *emblems* even, and he's *not* far from being a Fascist *monster*, all of which of course is grist and gospel to our own toxic EAW *too* few of whom have *ever* lifted a gun against the *Germans*, and if it comes to totalitarian ideas, I never *shall* spell that *ribbon* of a word, could give *numerous* points Haddock says to *Mussolini*, Haddock by the way struck an abortive blow in the Quit Bornholm campaign and asked the Foreign Secretary how *many* R troops there were there approx, but Bevin said he was not in a *position* to *say*, which considering that *we* liberated Denmark and *no* other is a *noticeable* circumstance you must agree, assuming of course which I do *not* that you have the faintest interest in the cosmic ulcers, how are the fox-dogs, and have you done a *thing* about the *briar-grove* for Haddock's pipes, I suppose you're madly cashing in on the alimentary situation, we're growing *spring* wheat in the window-box, and I'm *too* afraid I may have to sow *barley* in my little herbaceous plot, though not before the Boat-Race I *swear*, because my *bulbs* already are behaving electricly, it gives me a *pain* to see them, and yesterday I planned out the *summer* holiday, the old boat is back from the wars, my dear Haddock *towed* her back in a dinghy like the Fighting Whatisit, and we think we shall all tutter-tutter up to Oxford like we were going to in '39 but of course the septic Germans, there's just a *ray* of hope that Jack may be back in *June*, we've had the longest letter from *Tasmania*, which he *quite* loved, Haddock says it's the *most* cosy little island where all the names are *English*, I mean not *one* reference to Warra-warra, the only thing of course is that everything is in the wrong *place*, you motor out of *Cumberland* County into *Cornwall* and on into *Lincolnshire*, and as you go through Epping Forest you look up and see a hill which they say is *Ben Lomond*, *too* confusing but *enchanting* they both say though not *many* stone-throws from the South *Pole* one gathers, darling it's throbworthy to hear your Henry is really *digging in* at Rotary, but no my dear Haddock will *not* come and speak for him about PR or even Newfoundland because he's made an absolute vow against *all* public utterance *except* of course an occasional *special*, and even they accumulate *leprously*, yes my dear I know *all* that about *too* informal and say *anything* he likes and everything, because that's what *quite* everyone says, which H says is talking cabbage-water because *how* rude to merely rise and burble amorphously after a *free* meal, and as a *matter* of fact these informal jaws *nearly* always mean a morning's work not to mention *nervous* expenditure *frantic* boredom and dangerous *frustration*, because the whole time he's thinking WHY am I making this *dreary* utterance for *nothing* when I might be *winning bread* in the home, which in view of the little overdraft I could *hardly* second more *warmly*, you do understand don't you darling, and *please* tell them that if there's *one* place where deep down he's aching to utter it's the Rotary Club of Little Yattering, only you know he's got entangled in theatricals again, about which more later, and apart from that he's *embogged* in miscellaneous mush, for one thing it seems there's to be a *working-party* for the *publishing* trade, and H is beavering about

for there to be an adequate ration of *writers* on the workers'
section, because after all the authors are the absolute *pitmen* of
the industry, I mean *hewing* the raw material out of their
pathetic heads, but he says if they're not *too* careful there'll be
one speechless author on the w-p and *fifteen* printers binders and
booksellers, and besides it seems they have the *most* rodent
grievances, my dear thirteen books counting as a *dozen* and so
on, as Haddock says *what* would the Income-Tax bandits say
about counting thirteen *pounds* as a dozen, then of course *no*
Three Years' Average which means if a book takes *three* years to
write and then goes well you're taxed like *Croesus*, and of
course *no* allowance for wear and tear of machinery and *plant*,
the creaking brain and body I mean, which I think is *so* savage
to *all* professionals, take *doctors*, my dear if a soap-maker's ill the
soap-factory goes on *churning* out the soap and the income
flows *continuous*, but if Haddock or the *doctor*'s ill the whole
works *stops*, besides which he says the soap-chap keeps on
making the *same* soap whereas he has to think out something
new every *day*, so he ought to be taxed *too* differently and have
the *largest* allowance for wear and *tear*, though whether all this
will be in order at the *working-party*, but he says why not it's
part of the *export* drive and if you give the authors a *square* deal
and quantities of paper they'll do as well as *whisky*, and it's *too*
true that in Copenhagen there were masses of English books,
only *all* fabricated in Sweden or the Yankland, then he says
there's a rumour they're thinking of having a *standard* book for
export, because HM Gov thinks the present system is *too*
ununiform and anti-economic, I mean all these *different* authors
writing *different* books for *different* publishers, and of course
they all have to have *different* type and covers and everything,
whereas of course if you had about *one* standard British book
every *year* it would save *yards* of expense and could be *mass-
produced* with the *same* cover and a foreword by S Cripps or
H Morrison, which though *eager* to cooperoperate, that's
another pest of a word, Haddock is not *too* sure would be a

wonderworthy idea, because *which* book S Cripps would choose to be the *standard*, personally, of course I think it's *too* likely the whole thing will be *nationalized*, because at the present rate after *about* two years there'll be nothing else *to* nationalize, Haddock I suppose will have to clock in daily at the Ministry of Fiction and Fun which if *no* smoking's allowed will do him *lots* of good, anyhow now perhaps you do understand about the speech darling, farewell there is *ice* on the newt-pond but *two* rose-buds in the next bed, *too* symbolic, your subvernal TOPSY.

LETTER XXII

HADDOCK IN TROUBLE

March 20, 1946.

Trix my little winter-cabbage there's rather a bizarre yellow *gleam* in the garden which Haddock says is the *sun*, I shouldn't know, I'm still a *walking* refrigerator, all the same *deep* down I do feel the old bones stirring somewhat, like something you've had at the back of the fridge so long you've *forgotten* it, for one thing we're all talking about the *Boat Race* which is the absolute *herald* of the Spring in these parts and *quite* the maddest event of the year which I think is *so* suitable, though of course Haddock says if coal gets any *shorter* in supply the 8-oared boat may very soon be a *major* element in London *transport*, then my dear we had an *electric* evening when the *Ballet* opened, which really *did* feel like the bad days dying, *everybody* there one's ever known and the *entire* Cabinet relaxing bless them, we had a sisterly Scotch with Herbert Morrison who I *rather* think was *rather* attracted, HM by the way Haddock says was *so* boracic and brotherly in the House the other day that half the Tories wanted to *cry*, which is more than can be said of my volcanic *Nye* who I *do* so want to see build *masses* of homes only they say he has congenital *polemicomania* and even if you *agree* with him it's a Tory *plot*, and as for *rudeness* is not the poor PM's *top* ambassador for the *Dunkirk* spirit, however *what* a job and it's somewhat wonder-worthy that *all* the Ministers are not stark *staring*, Haddock by the way went practically *certifiable* about the *Lilac Fairy* and was *incandescent* for several hours because she got no *flowers* at the end, he swore he'd go again the *next* day with a *lorryload* of vegetation and I *quite* feared a cosmic scandal, however *fortunately* he had to play in a *skittles* match at the local, which if you ever *do* penetrate to the capital you *must* see, they throw the *most* ponderous *cheeses* weighing eleven or twelve pounds, I can scarcely *lift* one, and though Haddock thought perhaps it was *too* old-fashioned and laborious for the Century of the Common Man, as a *matter* of fact the interest is *dynamic* and they have *more* members than ever before the *war*, which only shows, though of course whether a *rust-encrusted* warhorse like Haddock, because this week he had his *first* instalment of *sciatica*, and what with *three* speeches in *two* days, *four* visits to the fang-man, and five hours at his bonesetter's, my *dear* what a week, *incessant* umbrage, nor *can* I blame him, because my dear those *speeches*, one about the suffering *artists*, and one in a pub about *what* he wasn't *too* sure, and one to an absolute *battalion* of doctors, and in between *hobbling* through the snowy streets from the *tusk-man* to the *bone-man* with sciatica and *no* hat and my dear tottering home in such a *typhoon* of a temper that my *one* hope was to remind him of the Lilac *Fairy*, and even *she*, however meanwhile this *magical* bone-man, who Haddock *swears* by and I did once go to myself about my *barbarous* rheumatism, and my dear there's *no* doubt he is a *sorcerer*, but *too* alarming for the tender *doe*, because first of all he reduces you to a cinder with radiant *rays*, followed by *inhuman* massage, my dear if there *is* a soft spot or malignant *nodule* in the shrinking frame he *finds* it and *grinds* it, *agony*, then he says Relax *utterly* and pulls *both* legs off, or *else* which is worse he folds them up singly behind *each* ear and snaps them off at the *knee*, finally he grabs you like a gorilla says *Relax* and *litterally* breaks your *neck*, you can hear it *crack*, the drab confession is that though I did feel *years* better I've never *ventured* again, *too* pusillanimous, however Haddock being sterner stuff the little wizard *quite* dispersed his sciatica in 48 *hours*, whereas *nearly* always it seems you're a cripple for *weeks*, the only sour note struck was when Haddock addressed the massed *doctors* he said he'd *just* been cured of sciatica in *two* days by a *bone-setter*, an utterance one gathers in about tact-group *79*, the abominable bone-men being like a stoat to a *rabbit*, anyhow Haddock says it's the *last* speech he's making *this* century, you did explain to Henry about Rotary *didn't* you, however we do not struggle *quite* for nothing, my dear it's *too* startling the Attorney-General says that the abolition or *modification* of the decree nisi is under *consideration*, my hunted Iodine Dale of course is *stuttering* with chagrin because her time is *nearly* up now and she *rather* feels she'd like *everybody* else to have the *same* degrading torments only rather *longer*, which I've told her is *not* a prosocial state of mind, because the Attorney-G says the King's P has only intervened in *161* cases since January 1938, which when you think of the *totals* Haddock says is *not* an economic *yield*, and *how* many *thousand* man-years and woman-months of *needless* frustration and general Iodine trouble *not* to mention toil and treasure for the law-lads have been suffered for the sake of *20* cases a *year*, the Canaanite at the Savoy by the way Jean says has folded his tents and gone back to *Canaan* to give evidence before a *Commission* or something, and I do not myself think he had any *long-term* designs on Iodine, and so far the King's P hasn't moved a *muscle*, meanwhile Iodine has got a sort of walk-on part in Haddock's theatricals, I cannot *clearly* envisage *why*, being my dear *completely* tone-deaf and can *not* I believe distinguish between God Save and Danny Boy, of course I *know* they want a few dumb lovelies and statelies for the *Palace* scene, but I should *not* have said that Iodine was up to *that* standard would you darling, I mean stateliness is *one* thing but *anaemia* is another, and I never noticed till the other day on the stage that one shoulder is *much* lower than the other and the *knees* definitely do not meet *at all*, however fortunately it seems she's to have the *longest* dresses, and my enchanting Mr Figg who's putting it on knows best no *doubt*, I must say she did *quite* a convincing slink across the stage at the audition and the competition was *not* severe, my dear have you *ever* been to an audition, *don't*, my dear it tears the *tummy* out of you, the *swarms* of personnel of *all* sexes merely *aching* to be in the *chorus*, they all bring *interminable* songs, and of course there's *no* time to hear them *all* through into the third verse or even the *second*, so they have to be stopped *half-way*, which though done with *loud* Thankyou's and *courtly* politeness must be *too* wounding to the *auditionee*, especially as *quite* often she's on her *top* note, the utter *apex* of the verse and everything, with her mouth *wide* open and her *soul* soaring about her *dreams* and what-not when the *suffering* musical man can bear no more the said top-notes being *yards* out of tune, he gives a signal like an executioner, the stage-man *claps* and the poor sweet's muted in *mid-yell*, *too* embarrassing, my dear *I* sat in *tears* with *Mrs* Figg whose bosom is *even* tenderer than *mine*, and whenever some *pathetic* tenor was cut off by that *stony-stomached* man at the *climax* of one of our *favourite* songs, my dear like *Jerusalem* or the *Lost* Chord she'd whisper wistfully But I thought he was such a *nice* tenor, or Didn't you think he was a *sweet* man I should have liked to hear *all* seven verses, and my dear I was *quite* with her always, on the other hand of course that was only *one* audition and the brutal management has had to hear about *twelve*, and about one in fifty of the poor pathetics is anything like what they *want* I gather, so no wonder they can't take the *whole* of the Lost Chord *always*, not to mention that *repulsive* ditty about Dreams which is *almost* the only song that youth seems to *know*, one thing anyhow as Haddock says is with such *battalions* of *both* sexes eager to sing on the stage no one can say the British urge to *music* is dead or the *theatre* either, though when it comes to *Iodine Dale*, no darling *forget* I said that, it's cancelled *utterly*, with malice to hardly *anyone* your warm-tummied TOPSY.

LETTER XXIII

THE SPEECH SWEEP

March 27, 1946.

Trix darling, *quite* honesty *do* you feel that *parts* of this missive look less unreadable than sometimes, because my dear I'm using my magical new *pen*, which is *such* rapture *British* made and even now I do not utterly *believe* it, you know what *torment* a fountain-pen can be, all those *sordid* little pumps and bottles, either there is a *total* drought or *floods* of ink in all your quarters, whereas with this my dear there's *no* nib only a *ball*-bearing they say though *why*, and no inkwork whatever, it merely *flows* out supernaturally for weeks and weeks, and by the way no *blotting paper* because it dries the same *second*, my dear it's *wonder*-work, so that in these days when there's *snow* in the drawing-room one can *huddle* in a chair over the embers if any and write untramelled, *how* many l's, by the normal nonsense, and by the way the whole thing is pretty Heavensent because of Haddock's experiments in *smoking* blotting-paper in case no Loan, he's now trying a mixture of *shredded* blotch and pencil shavings with a little *chopped* bayleaf *boiled* in onionwater, as a *result* of which, at least *I* say, he's having long-term *tusk-trouble* besides the most *enigmatic* swelling on the jaw where there were *no* tusks extant, because of course poor sweet the survivors are *too* few and could be counted on *one* hand, and a *half* perhaps, and from what one gathers the dentist would gaily eliminate the *lot*, because there's no doubt they have a congenital *contempt* for *Nature's* teeth, and I should say *Too* right, *what* an inept and *sadistic* arrangement, however H rather hankers for his *scanty* native gnawers because of the *pipe*, besides which it seems he has a concrete *jaw* from which it's *too* impossible to excavate the fangs without *explosives* especially if the tusk disintegrates, once my dear during the late conflict he had one hour and a *quarter* under a local what-is-it, with the tuskman, who my dear is a *top*-wizard, *drilling* away *quite* down to H's *chin* and the anodyne running out at intervals and finally Haddock opens his eyes and sees him advancing with a hammer and *chisel*, which of course one's *heard* about but never *guessed* could happen to anyone one *knew*, well in spite of *heroic* efforts by the fangman not to mention Haddock an absolute chunk of masonry had to be left behind after *all*, so you can understand we're not *fanatically* keen on *further* excavations even with *gas*, because of course one's *too* likely to wake up with a shattered jaw or a circular *saw* in the mouth, then of course in these days the staffwork is *so* interminable because of attaching the new tooth to the denture which means hunting for *old* dentures among all the chaos of the blitzes, I have found his *tops* in a nail-box in the dug-out but the bottoms still *defy* discovery, talking of *extractions* there's *warming* news *have* you seen the suffering Russians they say are positively *quitting* Bornholm 5,000 of them and of course we're *too* sure its *primely* the Haddock Liberate Bornholm Movement, Haddock of course says it's *high* time Uncle Joe came to *London* because my dear *there* he sits like a great *spider* in the heart of his web thinking every *fly* that comes near it is a *wasp*, whereas in London he'd have a *fabulous* welcome in spite of *all*, and if only he could see all the *shelters* coming down the old *suspicions* perhaps might be abated somewhat, though *what* he'd think of the *Licensing* laws, as for the *atomic* what-not Haddock says it's *infantile* for him to brood and hanker for *that*, because after all if the suffering Russians are to have it why not *quite* everyone, and *if* everyone then everyone is *equal* and *what* is the worth of Russia's *Security* Belt, then of course *I* must say one is beginning to *faintly* weary of our beloved *Greeks* who seem to be *quite* incapable of adult behaviour and have got political *liver-disease*, but Haddock says they've been just the same *about* ever since the Trojan *War* poor sweets, altogether the Continent becomes increasingly redundant, and *why* Haddock says do we not get any *Hock*, because what is Germany *for*, and personally I think it's *too* right for France to have the *Rhine* and we to have the *wine*, because it's *quite* manifest we shall get nothing *else*, my dear if it had been the suffering Russians we should have had *all* the Hun-wine ab *initio*, *last* night I *confess* darling we behaved *unworthily* at a public dinner, though Haddock having fang-pangs I shall *always* say that there was *some* just cause and excuse, and as a *matter* of fact I couldn't *swear* it wasn't my own rather unscouty *suggestion*, because I've often *heard* about his Speech-sweepstakes but never *saw* one in all its deplorable *reality*, I must say I think it's a *diabolical* contrivance though with noticeable fun-values, well my dear this was a *Birthday* dinner for the Burbleton Progressives, well of course it was an absolute *concentration* of Progs the *most* unsucculent provender and *uncountable* speeches, my dear after *one* look at the list H said we shall be here till *tomorrow*, so we arranged this *sweep* about a dozen of us, the *principle* is that you draw for *speakers* instead of *horses*, my dear your Henry would be *thrilled* though I do *not* commend his trying it at *Rotary*, and then you have prizes for the *Longest* speech and the *Shortest* speech, one for the Best *Laugh* one for the Worst *Cliché*, like avenues or turning stones, and one for who says *co-ordination* most times, the *result* is that every speech is interesting *however* destimulating or yawnworthy, and *in* a way I do think the speakers ought to be *grateful* to the organizers though *that* Haddock says is not the *habitual* reaction when they get to know about it, the *discouraging* element is that Haddock will *cheat*, at least *I* say it's cheating and he says it's part of the *game*, well I'll explain I drew the first speaker, my dear I will *not* mention names because you know how *odious* I find it to say an unkind *thing*, but he is the *Ace* of Progs, my dear he can't utter the *noblest* sentiment without somehow giving it a bad *smell*, like so many of the top-Progs do, and quite *tumescent* with pomp, my dear an intellectual *carbuncle*, and of course the first speaker *always* feels he has the whole *night* to play with, so I was *too* sure of winning the Longest *easily*, but what was my dismay he hadn't oozed for more than *20* minutes was oozing strong and looked good for *40*, when Haddock develops the loudest *cough*, which I must say was news to *me*, and you know if you have tusk-ache all other troubles seem to *utterly* dwindle, anyhow he coughed *on* and *on* with occasional indignant *mutters*, and you know what coughing is *by* degrees the *entire* Proggery began to cough and mutter likewise, the speaker began to deflate *significantly*, and Haddock said *too* sweetly Speak *up* Sir *twice* than *which* he says there are few more sabotaging things to hear, and before I knew what my *fallacious* Prog had sat down suddenly after merely *24* minutes, *too* disappointing though of course a public *service* to the *main* community, well then there were two or three quite *sufferable* speeches by *minor* Progs, one indubitably in laugh-group 7 or *8*, and *poor* Iodine Dale I shall *always* say might well have got the Best Laugh Trophy because *her* horse was telling one of the *most* hoary narratives which Haddock says never *fails* to cause a roar, not *even* at the Licensed Victuallers' who know them *all*, when *just* before the point and climax H starts a perfect *barrage* of coughery and *claps* in the *wrong* place, *quite* killing any *signs* of merriment, meanwhile his *general* strategy was a shade confusing because I forget if I've said he'd drawn the *last* speaker of all who it's odds *on* ought to be the *Shortest* especially after a protracted *battery* of speeches when everyone is *supersuicidal*, so H on the whole was for spinning *out* the middle ones and whenever a man looked like being *too* brief he'd get an electrifying 'Ear, *'ear* from Haddock and yatter along *refreshed* for a bit, meanwhile of course we were having

the most *hissing* altercations about the Haddock behaviour and
was it the done thing and everything, nor would I swear a
binding oath that we were the best-loved *table* in the room, well
darling *about* dawn the *last* speaker at *last* arose, with Haddock
all ready to collect for the *Shortest* having nothing but 9 minutes
to beat, but my dear it only shows you *how* inscrutable the
hazards of sport *can* be, because *quite* soon it *shone* out like
several beacons that Mr H was on the *wrong dog, too* satisfying
my dear the man was the last President but *two* and *swollen* with
streptococcal utterance, beginning with the *babehood* of the
Club and *all* its contemporaries, my dear with anecdotes of *high*
narcotic content, then of course he wanted to *quit* Greece and
invade Spain, *that* kind of cantankerous *unreasoning* Prog, well
at that point to my *unspeakable* anger Haddock suddenly
reverses his policy and goes for the *Longest,* and though of
course the man is an open *ulcer* to him he noisily applauds *quite*
everything he says, with other *unpardonable* devices, I mean if
the ulcer said there were *twenty* thousand troops H pipes up
Thirty thousand and the ulcer stops to justify his figures, well so
it goes on for 23 minutes and I'm thinking I shall win the
Longest *after* all, because the man is *manifestly* weakening, in
fact he says the hour is late I must not detain you *longer,* but
then *what* does the *base* H do he simply *hammers* the table and
yells Go *on* go *on* go *on* Sir, *regalvanized* by which my dear the
pest begins on relations with the *Soviets* and carries on like a
cataract for 29 minutes, so I *lost,* my dear I've scarcely *spoken* to
Haddock since except I've *dared* him to do the same devilry in
the House of Commons, I must say it made him *quite* forget
about his tusk-ache, there *are* limits however, meanwhile
Haddock's theatricals are *trundling* along, yesterday they had a
reading of the dramma to the entire company, *too* gruesome
because my dear there's been a perfect *plague* of tusk-trouble,
the leading lady was *quite* speechless after having an *infracted*
wisdom fang *excavated* in hospital, the composer had lost *two*
fangs and could merely *mumble,* whereas as a rule he sings all

the songs like an *angel* and plays electricly, the musical director
had *two* out likewise and still having fang-pangs, Haddock was
minus *one* merely but it seems the new denture has a *malignant*
trick of from time to time nipping the largest chunks out of the
upper *lip*, so in the middle of love-scenes he gives the loudest
yelps, and of course he never *was* the world's *ace*-reader, though
one does *not* dare to *hint* it, however all went wellish, but my
dear *how* any man can so much as *contemplate* starting a musical
play, the *protracted* torment, and when you think there's a
special *tax* on it, my dear a *normal* dramma is agony enough
when you have one bit of scenery *seven* actors *no* band and
ordinary *clothes*, but a *musical*, my dear first of all the composer
and the word-monger yapping round the piano for *quite* months
about *quavers*, though I must say Haddock and V have *never*
had a carbolic word, in fact they will sing their favourites over
and over *again*, my dear *no-one* thinks about an author's *wife*
who by the first night has been hearing the *new* tunes for
centuries, well then it all has to be *orchistrated*, my dear *millions*
of little notes, and paper *practically* unobtainable, meanwhile
the *pathetic* manager, my dear you *must* meet my *seraphic* Mr
Figg who is the *nation's* pet, is scouring the by-ways for tenors
of the right *shape* and everything, *not* to mention sopranos who
are not *too* circular, and of course the *moment* he's engaged
anyone all the *keys* have to be altered, and everything one
gathers has to be orchistrated *again*, at any rate the musical men
go about with *set* lips and unfraternal *mutters*, then of course the
chorus have to be amassed from somewhere which means a
campaign of debilitating *auditions* like I told you about, and
when an *authentic* lovely is discovered she's either got *quite*
nothing in the skull or sings like a beetle or has been *lassooed* by
the films, *too* discouraging, meanwhile the *scenery* they find it's
too impossible to change from the *law-court* scene to the *palace*
scene under *about* half an hour, so the word-merchant has to
write a *shattering* new scene about nothing *special* with none of
the top-actors who will all be *changing*, Oh and of course the

dresses, scores of bodies to be measured and fitted, for three or *four* outfits, *how* they get the material I can *not* envisage, then my dear as a rule *all* the principals want to wear voluptuous *evening* dresses in the *prison* scene *and* crossing the *Alps*, and there are the *most* incendiary altercations, though praises be not *so* far, and when at last rehearsals begin they all have *lethal* colds or *several* teeth out and crawl about in scarves and shawls poor sweets, *husking* a few words *tuberculously* now and *then*, and it's *too* dubious if any of them will be *audible* on the *night*, though as a rule they emerge heroicly, all this of course *assuming* that the martyred manager has got a *theatre*, which today my dear is like looking for a silk *stocking*, it now appears that someone has already written a play with the same *name*, fire breaks out in the scenery place and *most* of the Palace scene is a *cinder*, the LCC say that the *new* curtains are *too* inflammable and the censor wants to cut out the *entire* point of the dramma, then the band arrives which is *about* the one enjoyable moment only *all* the keys have to be altered *again*, so *chaos*, rehearsals *rage*, the play is *three* hours too *long*, the comic man gets *laryngitis* and I remember once at the *last* minute the soprano was stung by a wasp *all* over her *nose*, at this point the *complete* tribe and outfit have to be transported to *Manchester*, and *as* a rule war is declared or a General Strike *about* the second night, this time he thinks there'll be no coal for lights and they'll have to use *torches*, altogether he says a *Treasury* man ought to be attached to the management from first to last and after the *last* Dress Rehearsal the *martyred* manager should say to him, My *dear* Sir do you *really* think there ought to be a *special* tax on all this *agony*, however somehow or other the bizarre institution does seem to *survive*, farewell your philosophical TOPSY.

LETTER XXIV

THE DOGS AGAIN

April 3, 1946.

Trix my dumb darling unless I get the most *copious* letter from you *quite* soon I shall *terminate* relations, *one* utter from you in three weeks is *not* a ration, and that about your pestaceous friend *Fork* who Haddock says *No* he can *not* ask a question about he must go to a *lawyer*, and yes it's *too* right it seems a man can't marry his *divorced* wife's sister though if it was *deceased* but Haddock's out and *why* I have *no* clue about, as for *Fork* H said if he'd gone to a lawyer *ab ovo* he might not now be in such an inscrutable *mess*, anyhow there are *far* too many Questions nowadays and Members believe it or not can *not* interfere with the decisions of *Judges* neither in the New Era can they germinate *Bills*, as I *think* I've told you uncountable times, tenthly and lastly Haddock said *why* doesn't *Fork* write to his *own* etcetera Member, sorry darling for this comparatively *barren* response, but you tell me *quite* nothing about the children, have you done a *thing* about Phil's teeth, no darling *no* cheese has won through yet though Haddock had a *moving* parcel of tinned provender from an old flame in Dominion *Australia*, here in Parliament England, that by the way is the said thing now because of *Soviet* Russia, Oh yes and Congress America, well here in Parliament England a few *frightened* daffodils are peeping round corners, *two* newts are courting in

112

the pond which whatever the poets say is the first *sure* sign of
the Parliament English *Spring,* and by the time you get this the
Boat Race will be over, that is if *both* crews don't sink in a
snowstorm, and of course *why* they have *all* these events in the
rudest weather, school *Sports* for example those *mournful* waifs
in *less* than undies, with *bright* blue calves and their little noses
steaming like *horses,* and of course icicles all *over* the audience,
talking of sport we had a *hilarious* though uneconomic evening
at the grey-dogs yesterday, Haddock by the way is enraged
because they're putting a cruel *purchase*-tax on *sailing* boats
which they say are *Sports* requisites, though how they expect to
have a nation of Dunkirkers, and Haddock says if boats why not
race-horses and *race-dogs,* my dear what *mountains* of taxes
you'd amass when they sell those fabulous *stallions* and things,
and for that matter what about when Arsenal or Charlton buys
a *centre* forward for £15,000, than which *few* things could be
more like a sports *requisite,* anyhow about the grey-dogs, I
goaded Haddock there for the first time since '39 because it was
Jean Dee's *birthday* and I *rather* think he's *rather* attracted, *some*
bait there had to be because you know he's rather *aloof* about
betting, that is till he begins and then he *dives* in like a mad
thing, personally of course I'm a *congenital* gambler and my
spine tickles when the old tote starts clicking, my dear you *must*
come one day, it's *quite* decorative and rather *Roman,* because
you *dine* while betting and view the proceedings cosily through
acres of plate-glass, in fact a bookie comes along and *collects*
your bets if you like, so you need never stir from the trough
which would *so* suit your Henry, who'd sit there feeling like the
Emperor *Nero,* only then of course the whole party knows what
you're *doing* and personally I like having *secret* inspirations and
prowling up to the Tote myself, well when they turn the lights
on it's *too* scenic, like the largest *race-game,* the little dogs come
out and *march* round with six white stewards, and *parade* in
front of you, when my dear I *nearly* always have the *profoundest*
intuition about one of them, my dear you may laugh but I am

quite a *sage* judge of a grey-dog, only of course by that time one has already backed *three* other beasties according to the *form* and everything, I should say by the way darling that dog-following is no *idle* pleasure, one works like a *slave*, my dear I'd studied the *naps* and things in *three* papers, all *too* different, then of course some *wide-hearted* man comes and marks your *card*, quite different *again*, and then I have my last-minute *intuition*, so as a rule there are *few* beasties I have not got *something* on in the end, which Haddock says is *girl's* gambling, though if he's an example of *man's*, there are only 20 minutes between the races and what with collecting on the *last* race and deciding on the *next*, life is *asthmatic*, it's like doing an arithmetic exam against *time* not to mention *dinner*, one canters off to the Tote in the middle of a mouthful, the table is a mass of race-cards and *naps* and tote-tickets get into the *soup*, then they put the little dogs in the cage and the *fairy* hare starts circulating, and *when* my dear it whizzes past the cage and they *cataract* after it, *about* two-thirds of the little tummy stops working and does not resume till *minutes* after the finish, so after about three races I have *barbarous* indigestion however it's all in aid of the summer holiday, so one suffers *gaily*, Haddock at first was *too* lofty and *quite* content with Jean and a juniper-juice not to mention some *rather* palatable turbot, though somewhat vexatious about the *Betting* Tax in which none of us at that time could be *much* less interested, and after every race he would say he'd *diagnosed* the winner *at sight* during the parade, and if he'd been betting and so on, the bleak thing was that after the turbot he really began to *believe* it and started wagering in a large way, my dear talk about *girl's* gambling, first of all he'd choose two grey-dogs with nice *names*, you could *not* get him to back a beast with what he calls a bad name if it had a half-mile *start*, then he picks one because of its lovable *walk*, and nearly always he does Number *two* because it has a *blue* wrapper and he's sensitive to blue, then he asks what I'm on and invests in that *likewise*, so at the end he's on *all* the runners but one or two, *which* of course finish *quite* first, my dear *calamitous* because *till* then I'd been raking in *reasonably* and the summer holiday was about *six* Peppiatts nearer, but now Haddock is on my hounds not *one* thing goes well with them, my dear they're *jostled* at the bend or fall *fatally* at hurdles, the hurdling by the way is *quite* electrical and while they're doing that one *practically* forgets one's degrading *money*, there's the closest finish *twice*, my dear *three* little snouts on a half-sheet of notepaper each time of course I could have *vowed* that my *pet* beastie was first, though of course *too* prohibitive to be sure, because Haddock says by his slide-rule which I do not utterly believe in they're doing about 35 miles p.h., I should have said *sixty* myself, so now they have the *photo*-finish which is *absolute* magic, we saw the works, and in *quite* no time you can see a *dry* print, only of course each time my pet *intuition* hound owing to the *baneful* Haddock influence was *third* and out of it by *two* hairs or half a nostril, *malignant* luck, and so it went on, Haddock my dear wagering wilder and wilder and your little friend's winnings *quite* melting away, *what* Haddock lost has *not* been promulgated, all he said was that he would *not* have minded if there'd been a *Betting* Tax and he'd contributed *something* to the *Exchequer*, which in all the circumstances the rest of us did *not* think was Utterance Number *One*, Jean and her mate being downish likewise and quite unallergic just then to the *Exchequer*, as for me I have rarely felt *less* cordial to the Exchequer, we then withdrew for *solatious* draughts with some of the dog-heads, and the sequel is comparatively *nebulous*, only I seem to remember something being said about our *acquiring* a race-dog, I can not envisage *why*, because *where* are we to keep it and what will it *eat*, anyhow it's *too* sure to be last *always*, if you're *not* careful I shall call it Tongue-tied *Trix*, no more now TOPSY.

LETTER XXV

RADIANT DAY

April 10, 1946.

Trix my favourite clam I'll forgive your *wordless* letter because of your electric *news*, my dear it's *lyrical* to hear that you're coming to the insanitary capital, yes we can bed you for a *bit* while you're seeking stable-room, Haddock says he *thinks* he can tolerate you both for *about* a fortnight, but have courage I *dare* say he'll make it more only of course you must vow not to *utter* at *all* at breakfast-time when he reads *seven* papers and indicates his wishes with animal noises *merely*, as a *matter* of fact it must all be a benign piece of celestial *planning*, because Iodine Dale has *just* got her absolute at *last* and is packing *now*, praises be, so you can have *her* room over the river, no nightingales I *fear* darling but ducks and tugs and *herons* vocal, there's a rather *bleak* bathroom behind with a pre-Crimean geyser which fills the bath the *next* day, however I remember you and Henry are both *leisurely* dressers and Henry shaves at *dictation* speed, whereas we both detest the business and *scuttle* through it, in fact the first thing Haddock said was Henry is *not* to use our bathroom, so you might *tactfully*, I'm *too* joyful about Henry's new *job*, I should think for a time he'd make a *pet* Club Secretary, though won't he have to do *arithmetic*, Haddock says he's never *heard* of the Elephants, is that the club where they all have to have shot *two* tigers, and by the way what *will* your

Henry do without his woods and spinneys, there's rather a swampy island just above us all mud and *osiers* where Haddock says he could land in the dinghy and stumble about at weekends, only he mustn't shoot the *swans* which belong to the *King*, of course *how* you're going to find *permanent* sleep-space, it's *too* prohibitive, however we'll keep *all* eyes lifting, the one hope is to meet someone by *accident* at a party and *shame* them into a Christian arrangement with *cataracts* of juniper-juice, otherwise if it's only a hen-coop they want the earth *and* all the planets, the other thing is if somebody dies one makes *ghoulish* passes at the *widow* before she has time to *think*, only you have to be *too* prompt and pitiless, we've lost *two* good houses for friends because Haddock said it was the done thing to wait till after the *funeral*, it *isn't*, by the way can Henry do *carpentring*, because I wonder how you'd like to live on a *boat*, there aren't any, but they are going to sell some of these *naval* things they say, only then of course you can't get a *mooring*, it's all *fairly* difficult, here however I must say the general note is *buoyant*, my dear Jill has been decanted from the Wrens at last, *yards* longer and *quite* lovable, and Jack will be back from Australia in *May*, so with *both* twins you see we shan't have any *excess* cubic *space*, but darling you can imagine what a *spark* one feels, then of course I've *two* more fairy-tales to tell you, the first is after *quite* years of solitary servitude I've got *help* in the home, the *most* appealing and meritorious *couple*, my dear talk of working with a *whistle* they make the bees look lazy and *bored*, my dear it's *such* bliss *not* to have to do the front-door and the washing-up and cook and scrub *incessantly*, I've stopped already having the cramp *all* over, not to mention savage *heart*-leaps at night, honestly my dear one can not *envisage* what one's been doing all these years, and if the couple *ever* leave us I shall merely dig a *small* hole in the corner of the garden and *creep* into it without a word, though of course to you having weathered the war in Medicine Hat, or was it Moose Jaw, all this I suppose is merely *bat-song*, and the *second* fairy-tale is even more affecting, because my dear we *suddenly* discovered that our *lease* was up *too* soon, my dear have you ever the *faintest* notion where a lease is and as for *insurance* policies, well my dear our *sweet* old landlady came up to see us about a *renewal*, which she said she was *quite* willing about, and *then* she said, I'll give you *thirty* guesses, she'd like to *reduce* our rent, repeat *reduce*, because we'd had such trouble in the *war*, my dear when we'd got our breath again we refused *tearfully*, because the rent as you know is *not* ruinous, and she is *not* rich, far from it, but you must agree as Haddock says it was an episode of *cosmic* import, throwing an absolute RAY of hope over the entire human swamp, because *when* you hear of some of the stoats and monsters about and *what* they're asking for imperceptible flats and *mediaeval* cars, to hear this aged angel suggest *reducing* the rent, it was like seeing the *most* luminous rainbow in the middle of a *dense* fog, it does show you doesn't it that there are still *some* unrapacious and golden souls in currency, Haddock says there ought to be a *monument* to The Lady who wanted to Reduce the Rent because her Tenants had Trouble in the *War*, because he says if it once got public there might be an absolute *wave* of Christian dealing, *sane* prices would be asked for houses, Goering would admit that he was sometimes wrong, and the suffering Russians might give Poland to the Poles, anyhow it was a warming incident for *this* little bosom and the old lady stayed for the *Boat* Race, which my dear was a *radiant* day, I don't suppose you saw but *Oxford* won, *noticeably*, we had the hugest party and *stage* weather, *all* my daffodils and hyacinths came out unanimously *just* in time, in fact most people thought I'd been buying them in *pots*, Haddock covered the house with *flags* making the race invisible from *most* windows, the PM came and the Speaker, and Members of numerous parties all bonhomous and beaming with Haddock's theatricals and some dazzlers from the chorus, and of course *swarms* of ancient bosoms one had scarcely *seen* since the last time in 1939, *too* moving, though of course everyone invited brought *two* nieces or more, or an *old* friend from the country, so the catering problem, however the sandwiches which we began at *dawn* held out, my dear we were all mere *shadows* at the end and even Haddock had been *scrubbing* for days, however *nothing* mattered because it was the *Boat* Race again and a *magical* day, there was Haddock's old boat *still* afloat and in her Oxford blue again after *six* years of battle-ship grey, no more machine-guns and stokers but *alive* with *children* not *one* of whom fell in, *pure* miracle, there was the *obscene* spot across the river where the *rocket* fell, but now a man playing a *trumpet*, and there was the skeleton of Haddock's buoy where the *bomb* fell, and there *most* wonderworthy was the old house still erect with *all* its windows in and bursting with *congenial* people come to see the crazy *Boat Race* again, no one on the *roof* this time though because of the incendiaries and dubious *slates*, but altogether my dear it simply *was* the old world *creeping* back to life again, an utterly symbolic what-is-it, of course I hardly *saw* the poor crews *straining* their stomachs to get to Mortlake, one *never* does, what with *squeezing* late arrivals into non-existent spaces, and of course in agony about the *children* falling in when the big wave came, but I did snatch a glimpse of them as they *melted* into the mist, *Oxford* leading as I *think* I said, and my dear I remembered one night when we saw *two* doodle-bugs go by, one chasing the other up the river *likewise*, and we had *bets* about which would win, and I thought when *next* I hear some dreary unmagnetic ullage say *What* exactly have we got to *celebrate* about I shall say a few brief detonating *words*, fare well and bless you till we meet, your tough but tender TOPSY.

A P HERBERT

A.P.H. HIS LIFE AND TIMES

In 1970 the inimitable A P Herbert turned eighty and celebrated becoming the latest octogenarian by publishing his autobiography. Already much admired and loved for his numerous articles, essays, books, plays, poetry and musicals and his satirical outlook on the world, this time he turns his gaze to his own life and examines the events that brought him to his eightieth birthday – Winchester and Oxford, Gallipoli and France, and then, in 1924, to the staff of *Punch* where he remained for sixty years delighting readers with his regular column.

Alan Herbert was very much an Englishman and a gentleman – outspoken patriot, defender of the good and denouncer of injustice – and, in everything, he retained his sense of fun. And this zest for life that saw him through so much will delight readers as they delve into the life of this great man.

HONEYBUBBLE & CO.

Mr Honeybubble proved to be one of A P Herbert's most popular creations and avid readers followed his progress through life in APH's column in *Punch* where he first appeared. Here his exploits are collected together with a cast of other colourful characters from the riches of their creator's imagination. *Honeybubble & Co.* is a delightful series of sketches revealing some of the more humorous aspects of the human nature.

A P HERBERT

LIGHT ARTICLES ONLY

In this amusing collection of articles and essays, A P Herbert ponders the world around him in his own inimitable style. Witty, droll and a respecter of no man, the admirable APH provides a series of hilarious and unique sketches – and gently points the finger at one or two of our own idiosyncrasies. Such comic dexterity and inspired versatility is beautifully enhanced by a string of ingenious illustrations.

NUMBER NINE

Admiral of the Fleet the Earl of Caraway and Stoke is, as one might expect being an Admiral, a man of the sea. In fact, so much so that for him, all the world's a ship, and all the men and women merely sailors…

The Admiral's dedication to King and country could never be questioned – but surely it was a bit much expecting him to give up his ancestral home for the psychological testing of candidates for the Civil Service. Tired of the constant intrusion, and aided and abetted by his son Anthony and the lovely Peach, he embarks upon a battle of wits against the political hopefuls. The result is a hilarious tale of double-crossing, eavesdropping – and total mayhem.

A P Herbert

The Old Flame

Robin Moon finds Phyllis rather a distraction in the Sunday morning service – after all her golden hair does seem to shine rather more brightly than the Angel Gabriel's heavenly locks. His wife, Angela, on the other hand, is more preoccupied with the cavalier Major Trevor than perhaps she should be during the Litany. Relations between the Moons head towards an unhappy crescendo, and when, after an admirable pot-luck Sunday lunch, Robin descends to the depths of mentioning what happened on their honeymoon, the result is inevitable – they must embark on one of their enforced separations. Finding his independence once more, Robin feels free to link up with Phyllis and her friends, and begins to dabble in some far from innocent matchmaking.

This ingenious work brilliantly addresses that oh so perplexing a problem – that of 'the old flame'.

The Thames

A P Herbert lived by the Thames for many years and was a fervent campaigner for its preservation and up-keep. Here, in this beautifully descriptive history, he uses his love and knowledge of the mighty river to tell its story from every aspect – from its dangerous currents to its tranquil inlets, and from its cities and bridges to its people and businesses. Adding his renowned wisdom and wit to his vast knowledge, A P Herbert creates a fascinating and entertaining guided tour of the Thames, and offers his own plans for the river's future. This is the perfect companion for lovers of both London and her waterways.

OTHER TITLES BY A P HERBERT AVAILABLE DIRECT FROM HOUSE OF STRATUS

Quantity		£	$(US)	$(CAN)	€
☐	A.P.H. His Life and Times	9.99	16.50	24.95	16.50
☐	General Cargo	7.99	12.99	17.49	13.00
☐	Honeybubble & Co.	7.99	12.99	17.49	13.00
☐	The House by the River	7.99	12.99	17.49	13.00
☐	Light Articles Only	7.99	12.99	17.49	13.00
☐	Look Back and Laugh	7.99	12.99	17.49	13.00
☐	Made For Man	7.99	12.99	17.49	13.00
☐	The Man About Town	7.99	12.99	17.49	13.00
☐	Mild and Bitter	7.99	12.99	17.49	13.00
☐	More Uncommon Law	8.99	14.99	22.50	15.00
☐	Number Nine	7.99	12.99	17.49	13.00
☐	The Old Flame	7.99	12.99	17.49	13.00
☐	The Secret Battle	7.99	12.99	17.49	13.00
☐	Sip! Swallow!	7.99	12.99	17.49	13.00
☐	The Thames	10.99	17.99	26.95	18.00
☐	Topsy, MP	7.99	12.99	17.49	13.00
☐	Trials of Topsy	7.99	12.99	17.49	13.00
☐	Uncommon Law	9.99	16.50	24.95	16.50
☐	The Water Gipsies	8.99	14.99	22.50	15.00
☐	What a Word!	7.99	12.99	17.49	13.00

ALL HOUSE OF STRATUS BOOKS ARE AVAILABLE FROM GOOD BOOKSHOPS OR DIRECT FROM THE PUBLISHER:

Internet: www.houseofstratus.com including author interviews, reviews, features.

Email: sales@houseofstratus.com please quote author, title and credit card details.

Order Line: UK: 0800 169 1780,
USA: 1 800 509 9942
INTERNATIONAL: +44 (0) 20 7494 6400 (UK)
or +01 212 218 7649
(please quote author, title, and credit card details.)

Send to: House of Stratus Sales Department
24c Old Burlington Street
London
W1X 1RL
UK

House of Stratus Inc.
Suite 210
1270 Avenue of the Americas
New York • NY 10020
USA

PAYMENT

Please tick currency you wish to use:

☐ £ (Sterling)　　☐ $ (US)　　☐ $ (CAN)　　☐ € (Euros)

Allow for shipping costs charged per order plus an amount per book as set out in the tables below:

CURRENCY/DESTINATION

	£(Sterling)	$(US)	$(CAN)	€(Euros)
Cost per order				
UK	1.50	2.25	3.50	2.50
Europe	3.00	4.50	6.75	5.00
North America	3.00	3.50	5.25	5.00
Rest of World	3.00	4.50	6.75	5.00
Additional cost per book				
UK	0.50	0.75	1.15	0.85
Europe	1.00	1.50	2.25	1.70
North America	1.00	1.00	1.50	1.70
Rest of World	1.50	2.25	3.50	3.00

PLEASE SEND CHEQUE OR INTERNATIONAL MONEY ORDER.

payable to: STRATUS HOLDINGS plc or HOUSE OF STRATUS INC. or card payment as indicated

STERLING EXAMPLE

Cost of book(s):..................... Example: 3 x books at £6.99 each: £20.97

Cost of order: .... Example: £1.50 (Delivery to UK address)

Additional cost per book:.............. Example: 3 x £0.50: £1.50

Order total including shipping:.......... Example: £23.97

VISA, MASTERCARD, SWITCH, AMEX:

☐☐☐☐☐☐☐☐☐☐☐☐☐☐☐☐☐☐☐☐

Issue number (Switch only):

☐☐☐

Start Date:　　　　　　　Expiry Date:

☐☐/☐☐　　　　　　☐☐/☐☐

Signature: _____

NAME: _____

ADDRESS: _____

COUNTRY: _____

ZIP/POSTCODE: _____

Please allow 28 days for delivery. Despatch normally within 48 hours.

Prices subject to change without notice.

Please tick box if you do not wish to receive any additional information. ☐

House of Stratus publishes many other titles in this genre; please check our website (**www.houseofstratus.com**) for more details.